# BITCHES ON IVF

## TWO SISTERS TAKE ON INFERTILITY

Lacey Aumiller O'Neil & Lauren Aumiller Cronin

AUMILLER SISTERS LLC

# PRAISE FOR *BITCHES ON IVF*

"Sisters, Lauren and Lacey provide a deeply personal and sometimes raw account of their parallel journeys through fertility treatments. Their tenacity and commitment needed to build two families is inspiring. Journeys through infertility treatment are often tests of resolve and resilience when faced with sorrow, frustration and medical challenges. Partners, friends, and family along with the medical team are critical sources of support. Lauren and Lacey's account of their personal journeys remind us that with an unyielding commitment and sometimes using alternatives, family building is achievable."

—*Dr. Gilbert Mottla*

"This book by Lauren and Lacey is incredibly moving and it will surely be a source of support and strength for many other couples in similar situations. Their description of the excruciating journey to parenthood is intensely vivid. As a fertility specialist I feel it broadens my own perspective of the pain, the suffering, and the overwhelming joy that can be experienced by affected couples. It also made me reflect on my own."

—*Dr. Ricardo Yazigi*

"This sassy, irreverent telling of two sisters' struggles and eventual triumphs over infertility is fresh and insightful. The inability to have children is gut wrenchingly painful. The authors' raw honesty and vulnerability throughout their infertility journeys will touch every reader. Ultimately, their very personal stories of unwavering hope and determined resilience are inspirational and empowering. Bitches on IVF serves as an important educational tool for those walking the same path. "

—*Margaret E. Swain, RN, JD*
*President, Academy of Adoption and Assisted Reproduction Attorneys*

Book cover and interior design by Jess LaGreca, Mayfly book design.

ISBN paperback: 979-8-9893294-0-3
ISBN ebook: 979-8-989329-4-1-0
ISBN audiobook: 979-8-9893294-2-7

Aumiller Sisters LLC

Contact the Authors: Lacey Aumiller O'Neil and Lauren Aumiller Cronin
aumillersistersivf@gmail.com

# CONTENTS

# 1

# LACEY & LAUREN: BITCHES ON IVF

There it was—a super cute, fun, Facebook post from our friend Claire, announcing how "blessed" she was to be pregnant. We both wanted to vomit right on top of our phones. The two of us— sisters Lacey and Lauren—had been trying without success to get pregnant for years.

We are neither haters nor jealous women who can't handle other people's success. We've had plenty of success of our own, and usually we are genuinely happy for other people when good things happen to them; we love to celebrate good fortune.

But after so many disappointing years and failed attempts to get pregnant, it was hard to feel like cheering. We were both living in Annapolis at the time, a vibrant waterfront city in Maryland, which we both loved, but with one drawback. Every woman we encountered—or so it seemed to us—was blissfully pushing a baby carriage.

It was a Saturday in April 2010, the day of Claire's shower, an event we'd been dreading since the first arrival of the invitation. "I can't believe I have to spend another Saturday with a fake smile plastered across my face, holding back tears," Lauren shouted over the phone to Lacey. Lauren was always the more dramatic one, and the late night of slugging wine the night before wasn't helping her emotional state. She had done a few weeks of no drinking after reading various infertility books, and her new game plan was "drown my sorrows."

"I know, it's brutal. We are out of there right after cake is served, and not a minute later," said Lacey, always the older sister by two years, coming up with the game plan. It was hard to look forward to spending the afternoon admiring another beautiful, rounded belly, laughing at pregnancy and birth jokes, watching moms-to-be open adorable onesies.

That beautiful crisp spring afternoon, with the sharp scent of freshly cut grass all around, Annapolis was packed with tourists walking over the Eastport Bridge into town. All we really wanted to do was go on a long run through the Naval Academy, or out boating on the bay, trying to forget our infertility troubles just for a few minutes.

Reluctantly, we got into the car, driving together as always. Needless to say, our mood was less than stellar. We didn't speak on the drive there, each of us processing our jealousy toward our dear friend for easily getting what we had both been yearning for so desperately. Although we were genuinely happy to celebrate her first baby's arrival, we can't say we didn't both have lumps in our throats as she opened gift after baby gift at what seemed like a never-ending slow-motion shower.

"Is there a reason everyone has to squeal for approximately two straight minutes after every present is opened?" Lacey asked quietly under her breath.

"Ugh, I am going back for my third cupcake," replied Lauren, now drowning her sorrows in sugar. Although we were able to mask our emotions under huge smiles while we were there, the drive home was a different story.

Lacey felt like she had pooled every fiber of her collective being into trying to be happy, but as soon as the car door clicked shut, she was overcome with a sadness and rage she had never experienced before. Without words, she could tell Lauren felt the same—totally defeated.

*Should I say something and break the ice,* she wondered. *Maybe we would both feel better, or should I just keep quiet?*

For us, the best thing about being sisters is that we know, without saying a word, just exactly how the other feels. The silence between us that day was welcome rather than awkward. Sadness and a profound hopelessness filled the air as we listened to music, both of us caught up in our own dark thoughts.

Lauren was driving at the time, her hands gripping the steering wheel, as if on auto pilot. Her eyes were fixed on the road in front of her—seeing but not really seeing. She drove as if she were competing in a NASCAR race, creating a force field around us, and somehow moving all other cars out of our way. Her Jedi mind tricks were working. She wove in and out of other cars effortlessly. Lacey kept telling her to chill out and back off people's bumpers, but her warnings fell on deaf ears because Lauren was so focused on getting out of there.

And then it happened.

The car in front of us began to slow and Lauren did not have enough time to slam on the brakes. CRASH! Lauren's trance was broken when she woke up to realize we had just nailed the car in front of us.

We had been doing IVF for months and our bodies were pumped up with vials and vials of hormonal cocktails—hormones that at times turned us into emotional tornadoes. Things that would normally be no big deal became hysterical anxiety-filled rage fests, our hormones exploding in a kaleidoscope of intense emotional responses. Our road rage was coupled with "roid rage," and the combo was not particularly pretty.

There we sat, frozen in our seats as the offended driver furiously burst out of his car to inspect the damage.

In our defense, there was no serious damage, but this guy was fired up. He was pissed at being tailed for so long and let Lauren know it.

"What the hell were you doing, you are driving like a crazy person," he yelled at Lauren, scolding her through the driver's side window. "You've got to be kidding me, lady!"

Now, normally, Lauren would have stood up for herself (especially with the "lady" comment), but this day she melted into her seat, looking stunned—totally defeated and helpless to respond. The last thing she had expected was to get in a car accident. Lacey, on the other hand, became possessed as if by a poltergeist and leaped out of the passenger side door at lightning speed ready to defend her sister.

"Is there a reason you are being such an ASSHOLE, dude? Yes, she hit you, get over it, YOU MONSTER," Lacey spat at him. If Marvel ever created an IVF hormone-charged lady super villain, it was Lacey at that moment disguised as a 5 foot 4, 115-pound thirty-year-old woman wearing four-inch stilettos and a party dress while standing in the middle of charming downtown Annapolis.

One thing her hormone-blasted mind knew was that this guy needed to chill the FUCK out. Was there damage to this guy's car? Not exactly. Was he okay? Yes. What did this guy want from us? It had not dawned on us that we had in fact hit HIS car and that he might be upset about THAT. All we could process was that this asshole got in our way and was now yelling at US.

That is how crazy we were feeling at the time, the effects of the hormonal drugs rearing their ugly heads, turning us into belligerent bitches.

Lacey launched into a seething tirade, threatening his life as well as his male genitals. "You ever talk to my sister again like that, I will hunt you down and stick needles in your eyes," she said in a frighteningly calm manner.

"You chicks are downright crazy," he said, getting back into his car, wishing us better days ahead. The moral of the story: ya don't mess with crazy. Are we right or are we right?

A quick apology and meek wave on our behalf might have been a nicer touch, but we were bitches on IVF. Watch the hell out! We slowly drove away and laughed our asses off—until we eventually cried for the remainder of the trip home. We vowed one day to trademark a bumper sticker, "Watch Out, Bitches on IVF." Nothing heals sadness like finding a way to laugh at yourself. We were officially in this together.

# 2

# LACEY & LAUREN: IN THE BEGINNING

We grew up in the '80s in a small Baltimore neighborhood called Ruxton. It's the kind of place where no one locked their doors, and you ran into at least ten people you knew at the local market. Bob, our dad, was a real estate developer, and Sue, our mom, was an ob-gyn nurse. (Consider that irony!)

Our brother, Robb, was the first born, followed three years later by Lacey, and two years after that by Lauren. Like many first children, Robb was the favorite and definitely the easiest: smart, competent, organized, and dependable—the complete opposite of Lauren, the baby of the family, always attuned to her own drummer. Lacey, by contrast, was the classic middle child, a pleaser.

We grew up side by side with a Golden retriever named Bear, a typical Golden, adorable, super friendly, and dumb as rocks. Nothing eventful in our childhoods. Just a happy suburban childhood. Yes, we were extremely lucky.

We were all generally well-behaved, at least in public, probably in large part because of our Catholic-school upbringing. Just as our parents always stressed hard work and determination, the nuns and teachers did as well, and a little Catholic guilt sprinkled in here and there kept us on the straight and narrow. We definitely grew up a bit more slowly than kids who went to private or public schools. By the time we each entered ninth grade, it seemed to us a reasonable assumption that sitting on a boy's lap could lead directly to pregnancy. Ah, good old Catholic school!

Most kids growing up in Baltimore at this time were expected to play lacrosse, and lacrosse defined our childhood in many ways. We started playing on the same team at six and eight, and we quickly came to realize that not only did we love this game, we were also very good at it. It was the one place, on the field, that we weren't at each other's throats.

As siblings so close in age, we fought. A LOT. But on the lacrosse field, we sisters secretly loved being together. In fact, in high school, it was the one and only way we connected. In every other setting, we were like cats ready to claw each other's faces off.

"Those are MY socks!"

"Don't sit so close to me!"

"Mom, she ate the last of the chocolate chip cookie dough" (our healthy go-to snack).

Silly stuff, but we knew how to turn each issue into a major conflict.

The lacrosse field was where our real bond as sisters began; it was where we came to depend on each other wholeheartedly. We played on teams together, practiced in the backyard together, and dreamed of going to the University of Virginia (UVA) and winning a national championship together.

As it turned out, Lacey was recruited her senior year in high school to play lacrosse at UVA. It was almost an unspoken understanding that Lauren would follow two years later, and she did. Two years Lacey's junior, Lauren followed right behind her in many of life's experiences, great ones like marriage, and terrible ones like infertility.

From the moment Lauren stepped onto the UVA campus, Lacey took her under her wing and took care of her as only an older sister can. But it was more than that. Gone was the annoyance Lacey had felt during our growing up years. We actually enjoyed being together. In fact, we were inseparable, and soon people began commenting, "Do you ever leave each other's side?" Gone were the days of fighting and arguing, replaced by a mutual respect and deep love and connection that seemed possible only for sisters to share.

Lacey and Lauren bonded over lacrosse at the University of Virginia, 2000.

We were having the time of our lives experiencing our dream of college life. While playing lacrosse in college had its struggles, it taught us what it meant to truly be tough, both mentally and physically. Any setbacks or losses we faced only made us stronger in the end and ready to tackle our future struggles. Never did it occur to either of us at that time that infertility was going to present a challenge larger than any we'd ever faced before.

In college the goal was distinctly not to get pregnant. We could not have imagined that becoming pregnant would be one of the hardest times of our lives, testing our grit, self-confidence, and marriages.

## BECOMING DINKS

Our parallel lives continued to unfold on a perfect time schedule: we both graduated from UVA and moved to New York City in our early twenties. Lacey moved first in 2001 and quickly got a job at SGI Financial Services, selling her clients direct access to brokers on the New York Stock Exchange. She lived with four friends in the West Village, just steps away from Carrie Bradshaw's famous *Sex and the City* digs. Life was fast and furious, working hard and partying even harder, with little thought of what might lie ahead.

In her first year in the city, Lacey began dating a fellow UVA grad and lacrosse player, Ben O'Neil. Although Lacey and Ben had crossed paths over the course of those four years at UVA, they had each been dating other people and had never really gotten to know each other. When they truly "met" in NYC, it was a high-flying love affair. In short order, Lacey knew Ben was the one.

Two years later, immediately after college graduation, Lauren moved to New York to work as an associate equity trader at Goldman Sachs. It was a grueling workday, having to be at her desk before 6:00 a.m. (that meant 5:55 a.m., not 6:00 a.m.) and getting screamed at and ridiculed on a daily basis. This was way before

#MeToo or attention to workplace equity. She was expected to get breakfast, lunch, coffee, snacks, and whatever else anyone on the desk desired, from whichever restaurant her coworkers were craving.

If the *New York Times* said that the newest dive for chicken parm was up in Harlem, then damned if she wasn't taking a cab uptown on an hour and a half jaunt to buy 150 sandwiches. And God forbid if she got just one out of twenty-four Starbucks orders wrong. The reaction was predictable, screaming, "You don't have what it takes to work on a trading floor!" (Ironically enough, it was those baristas at Starbucks who would have made the best traders, working at lightning speed, calling out 15,000 orders and numbers at a time.)

Nights were spent entertaining clients at the trendiest hot spots, while trying not to get too hammered lest she miss her dreaded wake-up call the next morning

Lauren lived in Murray Hill on 37th Street, sharing the top floor of a large brownstone with her best friend, Anne. She secretly hated the lack of outdoor space and unspoiled nature in the city, but she knew that Goldman was a great gig and that she had to stay for the sake of her résumé.

After a weekend trip home to Baltimore, she reconnected with an old friend, Mackey Cronin. It was an electric reconnection that took place on a large dancing block at a totally sketchy bar. Mackey was Lauren's type to a T: tall, dark, and handsome, with a surfer vibe. He was adventurous and wild, and she fell head over heels. As soon as they started dating exclusively, the pull to move out of the city grew stronger. In love and eager to spend as much time with Mackey as possible, Lauren moved back to Baltimore, where Mackey lived.

Lacey, too, craved blue sky and green grass and especially proximity to her significant other, so she moved on from the city to Washington, DC, where Ben was finishing law school at Georgetown.

Before their twenty-seventh birthdays, both Lauren and Lacey settled down and got married. First Lacey and two years later, on schedule, Lauren. Lacey and Ben's reception was held at the Baltimore Country Club on a 100-degree day in August. It was a sweaty affair with the entire former UVA men's and women's lacrosse teams in attendance. The evening may have started out as a staid and somber church affair, but it quickly morphed into "Wahoos gone wild"—a reunion that almost got the Aumiller clan kicked out of the Baltimore Country Club.

Lauren and Mackey chose a different kind of venue for their wedding, Gibson Island. They both loved the water and the coastal vibe. The night was exactly how they had pictured it—both families and friends competing for space on the dance floor. There was nudity, blood (due to some aggressive dancing), lots of smashed guests and plates, a late-night breakfast sandwich debacle, and a whole lot of fun. The perfect wedding in their eyes.

For both couples, the weddings were followed by a couple of carefree years as newlyweds. Lacey and Ben both embarked on new careers, Ben as an attorney in DC and Lacey in commercial real estate. They moved into a cool, funky apartment in Logan Circle and began discovering the trendiest parts of Washington, DC. They made lots of friends and set about trying every new restaurant in the city.

Lauren and Mackey lived in downtown Baltimore and spent weekends either partying in their neighborhood dive bars or boating to dock bars in the Chesapeake Bay.

---

As fate would have it, both couples eventually moved to the unique waterfront town of Annapolis, Maryland. Lauren and Mackey moved shortly after getting married, choosing a row house in downtown Annapolis close to the water. Lacey and Ben weren't slow to follow, buying a house in historic Eastport, the closest thing to vacation living they could imagine.

The four immediately fell into a rhythm of hanging out together and meeting new friends. They spent happy-hour adventures drifting from bars to boats and formed a tightly knit crew with four other couples. Both couples were on top of the world, relishing economic freedom and enjoying the DINK (Dual Income, No Kids) life.

And then the time came to start that next stage of life—becoming parents—and BOOM! Roadblock. Not going to happen so easily, ladies.

# 3

# LACEY: FROM DINKS TO IVF

I can't believe it. For years, I did everything possible to avoid getting pregnant. I took birth control pills for a decade and worried every month that I might have missed a pill or made a mistake. Because we grew up Catholic, my mother's warnings about the consequences of teen pregnancy only fueled my fears. But now, I came to the shocking realization that I was actually unable to conceive. It was a strange feeling, to say the least, after spending so long trying to prevent it.

The time had come for the ultimate goal of my life: starting a family. But as soon as I stopped using birth control, my period went MIA. I was like a lost child, hoping and praying to God (thanks, Catholic upbringing) that maybe this month would be different. But I wasn't one to sit around and wait for a miracle. Oh no, I had a plan. And it involved a lot of sex. I mean, a lot.

My poor husband, Ben, quickly learned that sex can be fun until it becomes a regulated chore. And if you've ever been down the infertility road, you know exactly what I'm talking about. I became a master of tracking my temperature and ovulation, and if my husband wasn't in the mood when I needed him to be, well tough luck, buddy. This was no time for fun and games; this was business. Send me that sperm, stat! Heck, put it in a turkey baster and I'll do it myself. I'm nothing if not resourceful.

But here's the thing: no amount of trying harder or practicing could make me better at getting pregnant. It was like playing the lottery, except instead of a jackpot, I wanted a baby. So I scheduled my life around the times I thought I needed to have sex to maximize my chances.

What guy wouldn't love being interrupted during the Super Bowl with only four minutes left, his team on the brink of victory, just for a quickie? Well, my husband, for one. But he sucked it up because he knew how determined I was. This was my goal, and I was going to achieve it. After all, hard work always paid off in the end, right?

Getting pregnant was the next thing on my to-do list for my determined and hardworking self, but the universe had other plans. All those times I tried not to get pregnant, and now nothing. I was used to things falling into place and this, my friend, was not one of those things. My life trajectory was thrown off track and life as I knew it did not feel as "blessed" as it once had.

I could have sex around the clock, get acupuncture treatments, and pee on sticks until the cows come home, but there's only so much I could control. And that's when I learned that time was my ultimate nemesis. I was used to getting tasks done on my own schedule, but when it came to making a baby, I had to wait for time to do its thing. And let's be real, waiting is not my strong suit.

First stop was to my gyn who put me on clomid, a fertility drug prescribed to induce ovulation. I started taking 50 mg, then graduated to 100 mg, and finally hit the high of 150 mg, which thankfully allowed my dormant ovaries to ovulate. For any of you lucky ladies who have taken clomid, you know all too well that its side effects simulate menopause. A normal night of sleep, in those last two months, had me waking up at 3:00 a.m. in a pool of sweat, feeling like my body was on fire. I would jolt awake and sprint to the freezer, jamming as much as my body in as possible, in hopes of some relief. Damn, was I experiencing menopause?

Around the sixth month on clomid and graduating to the highest dose, I finally got a puny little irregular period. It didn't seem like much of an achievement to me, so after talking with my doctor, we decided that I needed a stronger protocol. Cue, bring in the big guns. Fertility specialist, here I come.

Fortunately for me, my sister-in-law, Jen, had gone down this road before and had a doctor in Baltimore, Dr. P, whom she loved. He helped her get pregnant with twins on her first IVF attempt. Now these were stats that I was looking for; two instead of one, on the first attempt, sign me up! If you asked me, those success rates would be more than sufficient for my liking. So I decided to set up an appointment with him, not taking any time to research any other doctors or fertility centers. As far as I was concerned, if he was good enough for my sister-in-law, he was good enough for me.

From the moment I stepped into the fertility clinic, I felt like a fraud. At only twenty-eight years old, I was the youngest person in the waiting room, surrounded by women who all seemed older and wiser. I kept my head down, praying that no one would recognize me, praying that I wouldn't have to confront the fact that I was struggling with infertility.

The clinic was a grim place, with sterile walls and fluorescent lights that made everyone look sickly. But the nurses, at least, were kind and nurturing. They led me through a series of tests, poking and prodding and probing, trying to find the source of my infertility.

First up was ruling out any medical issues with me or Ben. Af-

ter completion of these initial tests, I was diagnosed with amenorrhea and unexplained infertility. Great, that's helpful. Not. I
clearly knew I didn't ovulate or get a period and, guess what, now
all I knew is that it was unexplained (which I knew). Ironic, right!

I was told to cut back on exercise, gain a few pounds, and try
to reduce my overall stress—none of which helped whatsoever. All
healthy habits but a bunch of bullshit for a twenty-eight-year-old
going through infertility (or so I believed). Still, to this day, I feel
that the underlying stress of trying to have a baby is not something that you can ever control, and that stress takes a real toll on
your body. At least it did for me, but maybe I'm more complicated
than others.

After discovering my unexplained amenorrhea, the next step
was to get Ben tested and see how his little swimmers were far-
ing. And let me tell you, the poor guy had to go through a seriously humiliating process. He had to sneak into an unmarked,
shady-looking side door of the building and make his way to a
cold, sterile room that looked like it could double as a solitary
confinement cell. And his only companions in that bleak room? A
single chair, a crappy TV, and some less-than-appealing pornogra-
phy to get him in the mood. Talk about a tough gig!

Despite these less-than-ideal conditions, Ben didn't complain
one bit. And as it turned out, his swimmers were in great shape.
So it was official: the problem was all down to me. ME, ME, ME!
Honestly, I knew deep down that this would be the case, but it
still stung to hear it out loud.

Even though I wasn't ovulating normally, my doctor recom-
mended that we try a few cycles of IUIs (intrauterine insemina-
tions). The procedure was relatively straightforward. Ben's sperm
would be placed in a catheter, which would then be inserted
through my cervix and into my uterus. But despite my doctor's
optimism, I had a gut feeling that the IUIs wouldn't work. And
sure enough, they did not. I didn't waste more than one cycle on

IUI. After all, the success rate isn't exactly sky-high, so instead I decided to move on to IVF—in vitro fertilization.

All right, people, fasten your seatbelts because we're about to embark on the wild ride that is IVF. I mean, who has time for all that waiting around with timed intercourse and IUIs anyway? Not this impatient mama-to-be. So, I rolled up my sleeves and dove straight into the deep end of the fertility pool.

For those who need a birds-and-bees refresher, IVF means an egg is removed from my ovaries and meets up with Ben's sperm in a dish (the in vitro part) in the lab (some hot date, huh). The fertilized egg (embryo) is then placed back into my uterus where the whole idea is that it grows into the baby I so desperately want.

Now, let me tell you, IVF is no joke. It's like a full-time job, except you're not getting paid and your boss is your own body. First up, we've got the birth control pill, which is ironic because the whole point is to get pregnant, but I digress. Then come the estrogen shots, and let me just say, injecting yourself in the stomach every day is not fun. But whatever it takes, sign me up.

The hormonal roller coaster is real. One minute you're sobbing because you forgot to get milk at the store, and the next you're ready to pummel your husband for breathing too loudly. And don't even get me started on the physical side effects. Cramping, bloating, nausea, fatigue—the hormones can make the sanest person feel crazy as hell.

If you are lucky like me (not), you may also suffer from ovarian hyperstimulation. This is caused when your ovaries are working overtime. It truly feels like you are carrying around weights in your ovaries. Quite painful and very scary, I might add. It feels like an ovary could burst at any time. Imagine that as you are trying to work all day long, acting as if all is normal and good in the world.

If this doesn't sound pleasant, well that's because it's not. But the two weeks of fertility shots are nonnegotiable; they are crucial in helping your body to produce viable eggs and build up an optimal uterine lining, both of which are necessary to successfully achieve pregnancy.

The reward for enduring the discomfort of fertility shots is the grand finale—the trigger shot. This is the final injection containing hCG or human chorionic gonadotrophin. Administered only when your body is ready, this shot helps your eggs mature properly, marking an exciting, and much anticipated, milestone in the IVF process. The injection is given in your butt, not your stomach, and signals that the egg retrieval procedure is on the horizon. Thirty-six hours to be precise. This part of the process seems as if it is timed down to the minute.

Next stop up, the surgery center. This is where things get even more exciting, in my opinion. Here you're given IV sedation (yes please!) while the eggs are removed from your uterus. A process that is short and takes about fifteen minutes. The eggs are then transferred to a petri dish, where they are fertilized by sperm. After fertilization occurs, there is a brutal three- to five-day waiting period to see if the eggs develop into viable embryos. Assuming all of this occurs, and damn, a lot has to align to make it all possible, then the embryo(s) transfer is scheduled.

Throughout the entire two-month process, you'll be monitored almost daily with blood draws and ultrasounds of your ovaries. IVF is lengthy, time-consuming, and crazy expensive. It's a physically and emotionally taxing process, and when it's unsuccessful, it can be truly devastating. However, for those who see it as their path to starting a family, like I did, it's a process that's worth all the effort and discomfort in the world.

## IVF, HERE I COME

Bring on the IVF baby!! I am ready to be a mama, and I don't want to waste another second of my life being childless. Heading into my first IVF, I was convinced it would be successful. I would follow in my sister-in-law's footsteps and maybe even get pregnant with twins of my own.

I gladly took the shots, smiled through the endless blood draws, used my progesterone suppositories, changed my diet, ate endless pineapple and on and on. The ovarian hyperstimulation I experienced was real, and painful, but I remained hopeful and optimistic that my ovaries were working hard. So off to my retrieval I went, falling into a twilight sleep and dreaming about my little bambinos at the end of this process.

When I woke up, the doctor told me that they were able to get more than twenty eggs. Holy shit, I'm good! I felt triumphant and successful. I had finally worked hard and accomplished something, or so I thought.

Yet, my smug attitude quickly deflated as not all of those eggs were successfully fertilized. Only five of the eggs went on to fertilize and become good-quality embryos, worthy of an IVF transfer. (Which I know now is a hell of a lot!)

Six days later, following Dr. P's advice, I had one of those grade A embryos—the highest quality—transferred back into my uterus. I was convinced this was my first child. I began to dream about the two pink lines on a pregnancy test that I would soon take and how I would announce my pregnancy to my entire family. My line of thinking was this: How could it not work after the embryos were successfully produced and put back into my uterus? No traveling necessary for the little guys; they were placed exactly where they needed to be. All I needed to do was rest, eat pineapple, drink warm bone broth, and let them settle nice and cozily into my uterus.

The dreaded two-week wait (or TWW as I came to learn the infertility terminology) brought a host of emotions. (Did I mention this is an emotional journey?) After many ups and downs, reality hit when my blood pregnancy test came back negative. Oh damn, I thought, so this doesn't automatically happen for everyone on the first try?

I felt shocked and devastated, quite honestly. I took some time to process the reality of the situation and eventually picked myself up and dusted myself off. This can-do little lady was not deterred and I was even more determined. I had a lot to learn, and for better or worse, I was about to learn it.

# 4

# *LAUREN: TRIPPING ON IVF*

Throughout our lives, whenever Lacey experienced a life-changing moment, I would follow exactly two years behind. We went to the same schools, we made the same athletic teams, we had our first serious boyfriends both in ninth grade, got our periods in tenth, lost our virginity somewhere in there, went to the University of Virginia and played lacrosse, and got married at twenty-six—all two years apart.

So when Lacey couldn't get pregnant, I was worried. Scratch that, I was terrified. I needed her road map on this life journey. This was to be the main event of all life events, and I sure as hell wasn't going to do this one first. That was not how we operated.

While I may come off as the tougher of the two, that isn't the case. Lacey is the stronger, less emotional of the Aumiller sisters. We often refer to her as "Stone Cold" Steve Austin, the wrestler, as she sometimes seems incapable of tears. She is one hard bitch. Kidding/not kidding. But she also was the leader of the two of us, and I came to rely on her to show me how to get through all of those big life moments.

I remember seeing her off to college, my stomach in knots for her as we drove away from the dorm, Stone Cold barely giving the family a backward glance. I, on the other hand, was ridiculously homesick my first few months of school, actually losing my appetite for a few weeks. (Side note: it came back a few weeks later as well as about 30 pounds that freshman year.)

Still, worried as I was about Lacey's struggle to get pregnant, I figured that with a little bit of time and trying, she would accomplish this. After all, things had always come relatively easily to the Aumiller sisters. That is, they had come easily until now.

So we were both distraught when Lacey continued to have no luck getting pregnant. "It's fine, Lace, it will happen. Why wouldn't it?" I'd say to her, all the while wondering what if it didn't.

With every month that went by with no success, I started to wonder, *Will I also have these issues?* As Lacey eventually started exploring medical options, I began my own journey, expecting to have the same problem. Like many twenty-seven-year-olds, I had been on the pill for roughly ten years. And why wouldn't I have been? No doctor had ever warned me of the side effects of being on a medication like birth control for too long.

But I knew the moment I told Lace that I was going to go off the pill, I was basically doubling her stress, and even knowing how strong she is, I was worried. Not being able to conceive creates uniquely helpless and depressing feelings, and now I thought I would be adding to her misery. In her race to babydom, I was a new runner on the track, agonizingly nipping at her heels. Would her younger sister possibly get pregnant before she did?

Lacey and I feel each other's pain in the way that only sisters can. I was usually her source of strength in all of this, and now I would become a source of pain. My heart broke as I told her. I knew that it would kill Lacey if I were to get pregnant before she did. This was not how we operated; she was to lead the charge on this one, not me.

"Lace, I am not TRYING to get pregnant," I told her, "but Mack and I need to pull the goalie so that we at least know where my body is." Perhaps it seemed that I was trying to downplay our situation, but truly this was the plan. I simply wanted to see if I would be able to ovulate. After ten years of being on the pill, we wanted to find out if my body knew how to behave on its own.

"All good, Laur," she said, trying to hide the anxiety that crept into her voice as we sat eating our turkey BLT sandwiches from our favorite joint in Eastport. I truly felt like the worst human being in the world. She was going through such a tough time and I was only making it worse.

After four months of no period, my worry began to set in big-time. My gyn put me on a dose of Provera, a hormone that induces a period. Because I wasn't getting a period, I was clearly not ovulating. But nothing happened. I had seen the path that Lacey had been down for the past two years, and I despondently started to see myself following in her footsteps.

After a few more months of waiting for my period to no avail, I went to have bloodwork done to check my hormone levels. Unfortunately, the levels came back low across the board.

"So you can get pregnant on your own, but it is highly unlikely," said my doctor, not mincing words. In so many other words, I had shitty hormone levels and needed intervention. *No bueno!* While I could have taken a year or two to try to shift my hormone levels naturally by drinking warm liquids, eating bee pollen, or having acupuncture, I jumped on the IVF train immediately. Mackey and I began the months-long process of scans, tests, and procedures to see where we stood on the fertility spectrum.

And then we learned that Mackey had abnormal sperm morphology. (Any abnormality in the shape of the sperm—its morphology—can lead to infertility issues in men. Fun fact: 35 percent of infertility cases are due to male factors, 35 percent are female issues, 20 percent are a combination of both male and female, and 10 percent are unexplained.)

Mackey looked at me with concern as we left the doctor's office. "I had no idea my sperm could be the issue," he said, looking like a kid who'd just lost his dog.

"Well, looks like we'll have to replace you with a better model," I joked, nudging him with my elbow.

Mackey rolled his eyes but couldn't help but chuckle. "I'll see if I can find a sperm donor with better morphology," he quipped. As we walked down the street, we brainstormed potential candidates for Mackey's replacement.

"What about Chris Hemsworth?" I suggested. "He seems like a pretty healthy guy." (Google him.)

Mackey shook his head and smiled. "I don't know if I'm ready to compete with Thor."

We both knew that the road ahead would be challenging. The IVF process was not only physically demanding, but it was also emotionally exhausting. It felt as if we were on a roller coaster, with each appointment bringing a new wave of anxiety and anticipation. But we were in this together, and we were determined to make it work.

As we turned the corner and walked toward our car, Mackey put his arm around me and squeezed my hand. "Whatever happens," he said, "we've got this."

I smiled up at him, feeling grateful for his unwavering support. "And who knows," I added with a wink, "maybe we'll end up with a mini Chris Hemsworth after all."

We were told that we should skip the IUIs (or what I always think of as the turkey baster procedure) that Lacey had and head right to IVF with ICSI (intracytoplasmic sperm injection). ICSI is basically an upgraded version of IVF with added costs. It is a process in which a tiny needle inserts one single sperm into the center of a woman's egg. Traditional IVF takes thousands of sperm and places them near the eggs, allowing fertilization to occur naturally. ICSI seemed like a home run to me—let's cut right to the chase.

I suck at waiting and wasting time. I had three speeding tickets while driving with a learner's permit and tend to break out in sweat if the line at Trader Joe's is longer than two people (or if the bagging is not being done efficiently—don't ya hate that?). Suffice to say, waiting isn't really my thing. I want things done yesterday. Mackey would give a sperm sample, they would extract one perfect sperm, and voilà, we have an embryo!

If people were graded on how efficient they are at completing an IVF cycle, Lacey and I would most definitely leave the rest of the pack behind. One of us would quite possibly hold the record for number of IVFs in the shortest period of time. The Aumiller sisters like things done without a second to waste. We both were determined to succeed and every day that ticked by that we were still childless felt like a curse. So, we did what came naturally and tried to bury our pain and frustration in action.

I often visualize myself as an eight-armed octopus, gliding through my house, picking up four million pieces of crap that haven't been put away. I pride myself on being able to clean my house in three minutes flat, while at the same time replying to seven texts, because if you don't get back to people in thirty seconds flat, they might think you're dead.

I do not fancy myself as unusual; I am just a modern-day woman, people. As Mackey always says, "You women can get a lot of shit done!" And this was exactly how I approached my infertility.

My first round of IVF was pretty straightforward. I rode the typical infertility roller coaster during the stimulation period where you are given hormones to produce multiple follicles that will hopefully become eggs. This was the first step in the process. One day I would go in and they would tell me that I had a good number of eggs. Great! The next day would result in the doctor looking a bit concerned about the size of the follicles—shit balls. This went on for about two weeks or so until I had earned my trigger shot.

The trigger shot contains hCG, a hormone that triggers your ovaries to mature and release an egg. As Lacey had explained, it's basically the last thing you do before the doctor goes in surgically to retrieve the egg(s). What many people don't tell you is that sometimes you may not even make it to the trigger shot. Sometimes an IVF cycle may be going so poorly that your doctor will cancel the entire process and make you start back over at square one. Phew, at least on this first round, I had made it through step two of what seemed to be a million steps ahead of me.

So we get to the night of the trigger shot. "Ladies and gentlemen, start your engines please," I scream, as I pull the needle out of the wrapper and prep for the big event. Mackey grows pale and has to sit down.

"I don't think I can do this, babe. I am feeling a little light-headed."

"Dude, get your ass in gear and please stop being such a pansy. I have gotten nailed with needles for the last year, and I need you to buck up and be a big boy," I added nicely. I mean, this is his one and only job in the process thus far.

After several attempts, he nails the shot in my ass, and we slap each other a high-five, dreaming of all those little eggs that our doctors will be snapping up.

Next up, the day of retrieval. This is the day, usually two days post trigger shot, when your doctor takes a thin little tube, slides it inside your vagina, and sucks out all of those precious eggs. Can I get a "hell yes" for modern medicine, my friends? I mean, a doctor would describe it a bit more technically than that, but you get the gist.

I am probably one of two people on earth who love retrieval day—the other being Lacey. When it comes to procedures and hospitals, I can be pretty tough. When it comes to procedures that involve anesthesia, I am an all-out rock star. I love it, I love going under. I love waking up and being taken care of by the nurses with crackers and ginger ale. And I love the two days of painkiller-induced vegging-out that follows.

If I had an addictive personality, painkillers would be my poison for sure. For most surgeries, I try to steer clear of too many painkillers for fear of constipation and hemorrhoids, but I like to treat myself during IVF cycles.

Here I am, laid up on the couch in a quasi-coma while Mackey brings me my favorite deli sandwiches and selection of desserts. Again, I tend to make the most out of a bad situation and will always find the silver lining, especially if there is food involved (wine was also provided). Growing up, I could have had the worst case of the flu or stomach bug, but if it meant going to my grandmother's house for cold Cokes and grilled cheeses while my mom was at work, I was feeling no pain.

So after the doctors retrieved the eggs, they then fertilized them with Mackey's sperm in a petri dish. These fertilized eggs were now embryos, or "embies" as we sometimes call them. We were told that we needed to have at least one "A" embryo in order to do a transfer. Embryos are graded as an A, B, or C, with A being the most promising. But even when we got that little perfect A, it needed to stick in my uterus, and then make it through an entire nine-month pregnancy.

Just rehashing this timeline makes my skin crawl, and I wonder how I did not become a full-fledged alcoholic in my early thirties. I mean really, WTF. It normally takes about five to six days for embryos to fully develop, and some simply stop growing in the process. We got about ten embies from the retrieval, which then diminished to six on day 3, and then to two on day 5. Now that's what I call not a lotta bang for the buck, but forget that. Let's stick those suckers in! Mama is on a schedule.

Transfer day comes and you realize this next step in the process is truly the most anticipated, yet in reality it is also one of the most underwhelming days ever. In what is no more than a five-minute procedure, the doctor inserts a catheter into your uterus and then shoots the embryos directly into your uterine lining. It is a very straightforward procedure, and you can usually go about your day normally once it is finished.

I, on the other hand, wanted a cake and a bottle of champagne for God's sake. I mean, I felt like I had already been through a lot to make it to this point. Isn't some type of celebration called for? Not only did I not have to go home and lie on the couch, I actually was told that I could go back to work.

"Well, that was anticlimactic," said Mackey as we were walking out of the hospital.

"Right? I was expecting some kind of fireworks or something or maybe just a certificate of achievement?" I added. "A little recognition wouldn't hurt anyone would it?"

Next up on the roller coaster: the dreaded ten-day wait. Now most people call it the two-week wait, or TWW, but I had convinced my doctor to test on day 10. Of course! Is there anything worse than waiting? Well obviously, yes, there are trillions of worse things, but this really does suck.

First, you wake up the day after transfer day and the world is at your fingertips, there is a spring in your step. I found myself humming most of that first day, dreaming about what maternity leave was going to be like. Ah, the possibilities of what is to come! Mackey had even named our two embryos "Dude" and "Bro." We were telling people that IVF is a breeze. Really guys, it's easy.

Day 2 and 3 continued with much the same euphoric optimism and then day 4 comes, and the doubt sets in. What if this fails? Why am I being so sure of myself? Am I simply setting myself up for heartbreak? Day 5 had me constantly feeling myself up wondering if my boobs hurt (a sign of pregnancy).

"Laur, how are you going to know if your boobs are sore because of a pregnancy, or because you can't stop squeezing them?" Mackey asked me.

"Hmm, good point," I told him. "Well that means hands off for you too then." I bet he wished he had kept his mouth shut on that one.

By day 6, I was 100 percent convinced that I wasn't pregnant and by day 8, I was calling the office to set up my next round of IVF because clearly this one DID NOT WORK. Sure, there is a little part of you that thinks but maybe it did work. Maybe that little weird feeling I have is nausea. Then your logical self takes over again and scolds your other half for being so stupid and actually getting your hopes up.

Those ten days felt like a lifetime.

And when I finally did get the call from my doctor, I was told that my hCG level was 90.

"So Lauren, this means that technically you are pregnant, but in most cases with a number this low, we do not see the pregnancy progress," she told me.

A level of 90 is basically no-man's-land. I am not officially pregnant, but I do have pregnancy hormones in my body. Anything under 100 hCG at this stage in the game is not considered optimal, and we would have to wait another two days to see if my levels doubled.

More waiting.

Okay, so am I pregnant or not? Should I get excited? What do I tell people when they ask how it went? I feel like that athlete that finally makes her way off the bench, and right when she gets in the game, the whistle blows due to a thunder delay. I am so close. I am told by my doctor not to get my hopes up. So what do I do?

I do what any intelligent human does in this situation and turn to the World Wide Web for answers. Lord knows, you can find any medical advice there. After scouring the internet for two days straight and reading about every single person who has had a 90 hCG level and gone on to have a successful pregnancy, I realize that my chances are slim to none. Although there are exceptions, more often than not, 90 means a failed pregnancy.

My fears were confirmed when my levels did not double after two days. I was told that I had an ectopic pregnancy, which basically meant that instead of the fertilized egg traveling to my uterus and attaching to the comfy lining there, it got stuck in my fallopian tube. Treatment was needed quickly because my fallopian tube could burst and cause internal bleeding.

I was prescribed the drug, methotrexate, which treats an ectopic pregnancy by slowing and eventually stopping the growth of cells in the embryo. Your body then absorbs the pregnancy after about four to six weeks.

So my first shot at IVF ended in failure.

I was upset, but I also almost wasn't expecting to get pregnant on my first round—most likely because I had seen Lacey go through so many attempts and I knew better than to get my hopes up. Moreover, a small part of me was a smidgen relieved that I wasn't pregnant because I wouldn't have to crush Lacey with the news. Would she have been happy for me? Absolutely yes. But I also knew it would have hurt. Mackey, always the optimist, slapped me on the ass and told me we would get the next one. And so, on to the next.

This is where my compulsive "Let's get this moving" attitude really kicked into gear. I needed my hCG levels to go back to zero before we could start another cycle. I waited a few weeks and my levels were dropping but not significantly. This was killing me! All I wanted to do was start a new cycle as soon as humanly possible.

Finally, my levels returned to zero and I called my nurse and asked for our game plan. (If you think I waited for her to call me, you're crazy; I was not wasting one more day of being "not pregnant.")

The nurse laid out the next steps in a calm matter-of-fact kind of way: "Okay, Lauren, let's see. First, I would like you to go on the pill for one month to get your cycle synced and on schedule. Looking at our calendar, the office is extremely booked up, so we are going to have you come back in about two months from now to begin the next cycle."

Um, excuse me, I must have heard this chick wrong. Needless to say, I freaked out.

"I am not going to be going on the pill for a full month because I know that is not necessary, and please don't tell me that you can't get me on the schedule for another two months because that's complete and utter bullshit," I screamed, or actually hush-screamed, as I was at work and had people sitting two feet away from me on either side.

I literally felt like my biological clock was careening off a cliff and time was the enemy. But why? I was thirty years young. My logical self was telling me to calm down, take a breath. Give this poor woman a break, after all, my infertility wasn't her fault. She was only trying to do her job, and my crazy hormone-induced bitch self went for her jugular. After just one failed IVF round, I had officially gone to Crazy Town.

# 5

# LACEY: MY UTERUS RESEMBLES A PANCAKE

After failing my first IVF attempt, I hopped back on the saddle and planned to charge forward as effectively and efficiently as possible. And so began my second attempt, an FET or frozen embryo transfer, which was much easier than the entire IVF process as you don't need to produce and retrieve any eggs; rather, you transfer your frozen embryos from the ice freezer to your uterus. There is some regulation of your body and hormones that does take time to get to the actual FET. But thank God, no shots or enormous ovaries required.

For my first FET, or second transfer, we decided to put two frozen embryos in, since the initial embryo didn't take. I wanted to up my odds this second time around. On the afternoon of my thirtieth birthday, as luck would have it, I found out I was pregnant with twins, and I was dumbfounded. I couldn't believe the news when I got the call from my nurse.

For as optimistic as I was, I always had this little shred of doubt or reality that kept me grounded and realistic. But I had overcome this challenge—talk about an amazing birthday present. After hearing the news and telling Ben, we were so excited to share the news with my family over a birthday dinner of crab cakes (shoot, can I eat these?) and birthday cake. It was April 7, 2009, and my spirits were flying at all-time highs.

To celebrate my thirtieth birthday, I was supposed to be out having the time of my life with my best friends, but instead I was stressed out of my mind. Ben had planned this big shindig at our favorite local hangout in Annapolis, with killer cocktails and an awesome DJ. But this birthday was different; I was pregnant, potentially with twins, and no one except Ben, Lauren, and the soon-to-be grandparents knew. I wasn't taking any chances. I didn't want to jinx anything.

So there I was, pretending to be drunk and taking fake mind eraser shots, while my heart was racing with fear and anxiety. I couldn't help but wonder, *Will loud music and dancing affect the babies?* I remembered reading somewhere that calming environments and warm liquids help sustain a pregnancy. *Is this cold soda water bad for my uterus?* My mind was racing with crazy thoughts, and the stress was overwhelming.

To make matters worse, a bunch of my closest friends had come all the way from Baltimore and DC to celebrate with me. I felt like I was putting on a show, trying to act normal and have fun. But deep down, I was completely stressed out and scared. This was just the beginning of the mind fuck that infertility can be, and I was about to learn that lesson firsthand.

The following week, I returned to Dr. P for my follow up appointment, where he confirmed two tiny heartbeats on the ultrasound. He happily and officially released me from the fertility clinic and explained that I would continue my prenatal care with my ob-gyn. As I headed to my first appointment with Dr. B, my obstetrician, I was full of fear and had a huge pit in my stomach. Ben couldn't come with me that day so I had to face it alone. My fears and anxieties were constantly nagging at me, and I couldn't shake the feeling that something was wrong. Maybe it was a mother's intuition, or maybe it was just my nerves.

Dr. B, a family friend, was gentle and kind, but her stoic approach didn't do much to calm my nerves. She knew my entire history, and I could tell that she understood the gravity of the situation and all that was at stake as I hopped up on the examine table. It felt as if my heart were pounding out of my chest as she inserted the ultrasound wand into my vagina. After what felt like an eternity of searching, she delivered the news that shattered my world: there were no more heartbeats.

It was my worst nightmare come true—the loss of my babies. The news was like a punch in the gut, and I was left reeling with grief and disbelief. I was truly devastated, not believing this was my life. How could I endure all this horrible luck?

Dr. B sent me directly over to Advanced Radiology for a second opinion and to validate her results, in hopes that maybe they could detect a sliver of positivity for this pregnancy. Yet, even their high-tech machine showed that there was little to no blood flow to the two nonbeating embryos. I stared at the screen with enormous tears in my eyes, seeing myself from above and experiencing an out-of-body feeling. I felt so, so sad for that lonely girl on the table. It was surreal.

Through tears I asked the ultrasound doctor, "Are you sure there is no chance of their survival, like none whatsoever?"

She solemnly shook her head yes. I felt so incredibly alone at that moment and felt a tremendous loss, the most I had in my lifetime to this point. How could this possibly happen to me? Not only one baby died, but the second died too? The tidal wave of grief hit me hard.

# DARK DAYS

I lost the babies at almost eight weeks and while some may think that's early, losing a baby and having that dream ripped away is devastating, no matter when it happens. I later found out that I had been carrying twin boys, and the test showed there were no genetic problems with either of them. So where does the problem continue to lie? It was me. Again. My fault. My failure. My incompetency.

I felt ashamed of myself, and my mind immediately went back to my birthday party the week prior: *Did I dance too much or did the loud music provide a hostile environment for the boys to thrive?* The thoughts that went through my head seem silly to me now, but at the time they were genuine, and I believed them. Infertility can mess with your head, driving you completely crazy.

It had only been a couple of weeks since my joyous (or not so joyous) thirtieth birthday celebration. I had officially lost my babies and was slated to have a dilation and curettage (D&C) procedure. Many women need D&Cs after miscarriages; it involves surgically cutting out whatever embryo tissue remains in the uterus.

On a dreary late April Thursday morning, I arrived at the hospital, ready to put the D&C behind me once and for all. The one positive of this experience was that I got to go under again and damn do I love a good dose of twilight sleep. There is nothing better than anesthesia and those few seconds of bliss that you feel as you drift into Neverland. Like all good things, though, that quickly comes to an end when you wake from surgery feeling the physical and emotional pain of what just happened.

After the surgery, as I slowly regained consciousness, I could hear the sound of machines beeping and the soft murmurs of nurses in the background. My mind felt fuzzy and groggy, but I was relieved to have the procedure behind me. Suddenly, Dr. B walked into the room and approached my bed.

"How are you feeling?" she asked with a gentle tone.

"Pretty good," I replied, wincing as I tried to shift my body into a more comfortable position.

She explained to me, "The anesthesia can take a while to wear off. But the surgery went well. I was conservative with what I took out to minimize any risk of scarring," she explained, checking my vitals as she spoke.

"Thank you," I replied, grateful for her care and expertise. "So, when will I be able to start trying again?" I asked, feeling impatient.

"Well, we'll need to monitor your hormone levels and make sure everything is back to normal first. It could take a few weeks, but we'll keep you updated," she reassured me.

I nodded, still feeling groggy and a bit sore. The clock on the wall seemed to taunt me, reminding me that time was passing by without any progress toward my goal. I hated feeling like I was at a standstill, but I knew I needed to be patient and trust the process.

As we drove home late that night from the hospital, the weight of the world seemed to be crushing down on me. Each breath felt heavy and each movement was a struggle. The physical pain was bearable, but the emotional pain was a different story. It felt like I had lost a piece of myself, and that void seemed impossible to fill. It was a long road ahead, and the thought of it seemed insurmountable.

After my D&C, I was told I had to wait over two months before I could try again. It was a frustrating and disheartening time, but I refused to let it defeat me. I decided to focus on things that brought me joy and made the time pass by faster. I threw myself into running, spending time with my husband and friends, and even planned a much-needed getaway to Napa Valley in California. We indulged ourselves and used all our credit card points and miles to book the trip, determined to create some lasting memories.

In Napa, Ben and I rode bikes through scenic vineyards, drank a lot of really good wine, lounged by the pool, and feasted on amazing food. It was an escape from our reality and allowed us to de-stress and feel carefree for a few precious days. For a moment, we forgot the pain and the heartbreak and just reveled in the present. We truly felt happy and grateful, two emotions that had temporarily escaped us after the D&C. But as the saying goes, all good things must come to an end. As we made our way back to the East Coast, the real world was waiting for us once again.

It turned out that a two-month break from my daily fertility center routine was much needed, bringing me back feeling renewed and ready to try again when the doctor cleared me for my next cycle. Back to Dr. P I went with my head held high and my hopes even higher. I was feeling strong, resilient, and brave again. I started my next round of drugs in hopes of another FET.

After a few days of maximum progesterone to beef up my uterine lining, I was ready for a baseline sonogram of my uterus. I was feeling like an old hat at this point, and I had zero reservations about hopping up on the sonogram table and spreading my legs open; any embarrassment that I once felt had clearly evaporated. Naked happy baby pose on the sonogram table seemed as common to me as brushing my teeth.

As the cold, wet wand entered me, I heard the familiar beep, beep, beep noise of tapping buttons on the sonogram machine. Fingers crossed, I prayed that I would pass their test and be ready to move forward with another frozen embryo transfer. I couldn't help myself, and the silence was killing me so I quickly blurted out, "Is there a thick and cushy uterine lining in there, Dr. P?" Hoping to break the ice with some comedy as we were on very friendly terms at this point.

Dr. P smiled his warm smile, but remained focused and quiet for a minute. *SHIT, SHIT, SHIT,* I thought. All of a sudden, I felt that pit in my stomach again, and I had the sense that something wasn't quite right.

After examining my uterus for what felt like ten minutes, but was probably only three, Dr. P graciously suggested that I should get dressed and meet him in his office to discuss the ultrasound results.

*Why me, God?* The dread of what he was about to tell me had already set in; clearly nothing good was about to come. I already knew that I had been given the maximum amount of progesterone, so what could it be this time? I got dressed, bit off all my fingernails and walked down the hallway to his office, bargaining with God on my way.

My body collapsed into his office chair as I stared at him blankly while he explained as direct as ever. "Your uterus is scarred, Lacey. By scarred, I mean horribly damaged and closed shut. Your uterus should resemble a donut, with a large opening in the middle where we transfer the embryo. Unfortunately, your uterus resembles a pancake—flat with no opening at all. What I believe happened is that after the D&C, your uterus healed incorrectly. Instead of regenerating a normal uterine lining, it formed scar tissue. In fact, so much scar tissue that it appears to have filled your entire uterus. So now, the donut hole is nonexistent, and your uterus looks more like a flat pancake."

He went on to explain that there was a surgical procedure in which he would put me under (here we go again) and go in laparoscopically to cut out all the scar tissue. (Isn't it funny how they say "procedure" rather than "surgery" these days? As if we don't know better!) After cutting out the scar tissue, he would then insert a vaginal balloon, which would "blow up" in my uterus. The balloon, which would cause mild discomfort, would be kept inside me for ten days.

They hoped during the ten days that my uterus would heal properly around the balloon. If all went well, the balloon would act as a barrier preventing the uterus from sealing itself shut. Ergo, pancake. But, as he explained, there was no guarantee that this would work. And if it did not, I would need to think about surrogacy as an option.

Wowza, that term certainly hit home. To say the idea of this was unbearable would be a vast understatement. It was too early in my journey to even think about this option. I couldn't and wouldn't wrap my head around what this could potentially mean. For me, there was no other option except to carry my own baby.

This was a hell of a lot to process, but I took a deep breath anyway. Who could afford time to process this when I wanted to be scheduled for surgery ASAP. ASAP meant tomorrow if available, although now would be preferable. Because I was alone at this appointment, Dr. P politely suggested that I call Ben to discuss the situation, which apparently was far worse and more serious than I had realized. I agreed, but my mind was made up, and I was sure that Ben would be on board with this surgery.

I was not willing to leave Dr. P's office until surgery was scheduled for the following week. Calling Ben to deliver this news practically killed me. You see, my poor Ben had just rushed to his father's bedside at UVA hospital in Charlottesville, Virginia. Ben's father, Bob, who lived and worked in Charlottesville, had suffered an aortic dissection two days before. He was in a medically induced coma, fighting for his life.

The reality of the situation was too much to bear. I couldn't fathom adding any more stress to Ben. On top of his father's unknown health, Ben couldn't help but be incredibly desperate for our next cycle to work. Sometimes the pressure of it all bore more heavily on him than it did on me. I know he felt helpless at times and deeply frustrated that he could not bear the pain for me. As I started my drive to meet him in Charlottesville, I wondered how I could possibly tell him this horrific news.

Ever the delay tactic, and wanting to tell Ben in person, I decided to call my mom first. I knew she would be by the phone waiting for an update on my appointment. Unfortunately I also knew that telling her would be almost as hard as telling Ben. As the saying goes, "You are only as happy as your unhappiest child." This saying was made for my mom. Seeing me in agony broke her heart, and she is not one to hide her sadness. I felt it tenfold.

The thing about infertility that makes it so difficult for the woman is that in addition to enduring all the shots, appointments, painful surgeries, and other physical aspects of it, she also must be the bearer of the bad news, a painful and difficult task. You feel as if you are constantly letting down all the people you love most.

Because my mom was a nurse, she always wanted to know all the medical details. She was terrified of everything I was putting myself through. I kept trying to reassure her: "Mom, I am not going to focus on the negative what-ifs, but on the positive outcome. There is no other way for me to do it."

As I pulled into the UVA hospital parking lot three hours later, my heart was heavy with worry and anxiety. I knew I had to face Ben and tell him about my appointment with Dr. P, but I didn't know how to break the news to him. Ben's father was fighting for his life in the hospital, and the last thing I wanted was to add more stress to his already heavy load.

We had agreed to meet in the cafeteria, where Ben could update me on his dad's condition and prepare me for what I was about to see. As soon as I spotted Ben, my heart ached for him. He looked so defeated and heartbroken, and it was hard to hold back my tears.

I ran up to him and gave him a big hug, which was unusual for me since I'm not a very touchy-feely person. Ben immediately knew that something was wrong, and I could see the concern in his eyes. It was hard to keep the tears at bay, but I had to be strong and tell him about my appointment.

Although our situation seemed trivial compared to what Ben's family was going through, it was still an important part of our lives and future. We had briefly discussed my results on the phone, but I promised to explain everything in detail once we were together. When he asked for more information, I tried to downplay it, but deep down, I knew that the news was devastating.

"Yeah, so the doctor will cut out the scar tissue and put this balloon in my uterus for ten days, in which time my uterus will hopefully heal around it," I explained.

Ben's response was characteristically direct. "Lace, tell me what happens if it doesn't heal?"

I tried to sugarcoat it. "Uh, I'm not sure," I responded. "But I am sure it will."

Ben wasn't convinced. "Lace, we need to know what our options are if it doesn't work. We can't just hope for the best and ignore the worst-case scenario."

I knew he was right, but I didn't want to face it. "I can't even think about that right now, Ben," I said, my voice breaking. "I just want to focus on the surgery and getting better."

Ben took my hand and looked me in the eyes. "We will get through this together, Lace. Whatever happens, we will face it together."

His words brought a small sense of comfort, but the reality of our situation still weighed heavily on me. How would we handle it if the surgery didn't work? Would we ever be able to have a baby? The uncertainty was almost too much to bear.

As the reality of the situation set in, Ben was on the verge of tears, and rightfully so. How could one person endure so much pain in one day? His demeanor went from bad to worse. Over a pizza lunch later that day at Mellow Mushroom, he was able to voice his concerns and worries for me. He hated seeing me go through so many surgeries, constantly putting my body through pain.

This was a time when I very clearly stepped up and did what I do best—acting as the optimist. I had come to realize that there were only two ways to go with my infertile self, and optimism was definitely the better route. This lunch was yet another turning point for us; we were reminded that we had each other and together we would figure this out.

To help put Ben at ease, I reminded him, "Honestly, nothing scares me, babe," I tried to reassure him. "No surgery, no shot, nothing. I just want a family. I can take physical pain, that's truly the easiest part of all of this."

The bitter reality of growing up had hit us hard as we walked back down UVA's Main Street toward the hospital. No longer were we carefree college students, but rather adults facing life-altering challenges. We were no longer playing a game on the lacrosse field, but rather playing a game of life and death in the hospital. Ben's dad was still not out of the woods, but he had taken a turn for the better in the last few hours. Still, our college days seemed so far off. How was it only a decade ago that our biggest worry in the world was how much playing time we got? We had come a long way since those partying college days and it wasn't lost on us.

Despite the hardships, we found comfort in each other's company, holding hands tightly as we walked back to face the unknown. It was a moment of clarity, a realization that life is unpredictable and that we must take it one step at a time. As we walked, we talked about the future, and we reaffirmed our commitment to each other and our dreams of having a family. We may not have known what the future holds, but we knew that we had each other and that we were stronger together. We vowed to focus on the present and take things one day at a time. Or as I like to think, one procedure at a time.

## AND THEN THE SUNSHINE

Thankfully, things improved with my father-in-law, and we were back at home facing our new reality and this unknown path that we would have to navigate. As I prepared for yet another surgery, which would require that I take some time off work, I knew we needed some sunshine in our lives. It was mid-February: dark, cold, and freaking dreary as hell in Maryland. So we planned a long-weekend trip to Naples, Florida, to visit my parents, who were spending the winter there.

My surgery was scheduled for a Wednesday, the day before we were to fly down to Florida. A few of my nurses suggested we wait a few days to leave in case there were complications from the surgery, but I would hear nothing of it. I am a summer, beach-loving, sunshine kind of girl, and I married a golf-fanatic, warm weather-loving man. I knew that the best medicine for us was a trip with palm trees, green grass, and sunshine. Frankly, if a complication arose, there were hospitals in Naples, people!

All went well in the surgery and Dr. P wished me good fortune and healthy healing. He also mentioned that now the waiting game began. Oh yeah, like just NOW? I felt like I had been waiting for years at this point. What I didn't quite grasp was the magnitude of this waiting period. This was a biggie and would determine if my uterus would ever recover and be able to carry a pregnancy. But if we had to play a waiting game, it was going to happen on my terms, so off to Florida we went.

Landing in the Sunshine State, I immediately felt a sense of relief walking off the Southwest plane, the humidity warming me to my core. My dad, with his carefree attitude and easy-going smile, was a welcome sight as he picked us up at the airport to take us to their condominium.

Once we arrived and changed into warm weather clothes, we were ready to relax with dinner out on the town. The four of us headed to a charming little Italian restaurant called BiCE. I will never forget that first night, in my uncomfortable, bloated state, sitting outside, eating made-from-scratch Italian food, and sipping wine. I had never appreciated the warm weather and endorphins it produces as much as I did that first evening.

After a strong cocktail, I was finally able to unwind and truly relax. I vowed to myself to think positively throughout the next ten days, balloon in me and all. A word or two on this balloon that was blown up inside of me. Just to add a bit of a visual, there was a cord that was attached to the uterine balloon. This cord was used to deflate the balloon when the time came to remove it from my uterus. The cord literally hung out of my vagina and was medically taped to my leg. So you can only imagine how fun going to the beach was on this trip. Imagine the biggest imaginable tampon falling out of your vagina with an incredibly thick string attached. And man did I not want it to fall out.

I walked on eggshells, bleeding nonstop, hoping it wouldn't slip out (which was another ridiculous thought). I lay around the pool a lot, wearing a coverup to hide the vaginal cord tucked into in a large, padded bathing suit bottom. All the discomfort and fear aside, I reveled in the much-needed sunshine and relaxation. There was truly no better healing for me than a good dose of vitamin D (and quite a few rum punches). A few days in one of our happy places was just what the doctor ordered.

After our trip to Florida, we returned to Annapolis feeling energized. The medical team removed the balloon, and we were told that it would take some time to see how my uterus would heal.

Despite this uncertainty, I resumed my weekly acupuncture sessions, which I had grown to love. Camilla, my acupuncturist, had become not only one of my best friends but also one of my biggest confidants during this time. I cannot express how much I relied on her and how grateful I am for her support. Though I enjoyed the therapeutic benefits of acupuncture, it was Camilla's compassionate ear and heart that kept me coming back every week.

She listened to me week after week and became a therapist in many ways. Her calm and positive demeanor, combined with a new program called Heal from Within were two sources of strength that allowed me to navigate through the tough times and prepare myself for all that was to come on my journey.

# HEALING FROM WITHIN

Going through infertility can be a difficult and isolating experience, and that's why I highly recommend mindfulness programs to anyone in a similar situation. In my case, I was fortunate to discover the Heal from Within program, which was designed specifically for women struggling with infertility in the Washington, DC, area.

Although it was initially difficult to summon the courage to attend the workshop and meet with a group of strangers week after week, it turned out to be an incredibly empowering experience. The program, along with my weekly acupuncture sessions, helped me navigate the emotional challenges of infertility and prepare for what was to come. At the time, in the fall of 2010, infertility was not as openly discussed as it is today, so finding this community of support was a true gift.

In addition, at the time, meditation and mindfulness were not widely utilized coping techniques like they are today. Being a reserved person, I felt uncomfortable opening up and doing meditation with people I didn't know. And having to pour my heart out to them, well that was a whole other story. Nevertheless, I was determined to try anything that could help me through my infertility struggles.

As I attended the ten-week workshop, I began to feel more centered and calmer. Instead of constantly worrying about the future, I started focusing on the present moment, of being in the moment. I tried to stop stressing over the clock and how long it was taking me to achieve my dream. And the greatest gift of all was the ability to share my story with others going through similar experiences. It was invaluable and tremendously comforting.

I began to look forward to the hour-long, twenty-five-mile commute into DC every Wednesday evening after work, just to be with this random group of strangers. In the appropriately named

"Heal from Within" program, we learned so many valuable techniques including how to meditate, how to be mindful and present, what foods were preferable to sustain a pregnancy, coping mechanisms for loss, and much more.

One of the more helpful and introspective activities we were assigned was to write a letter to ourselves. This letter was supposed to detail where we hoped our lives would be in a year's time. Our group leader would send it to us one year later, to the day. Fifteen years later, I still keep that letter in my bedside table as a reminder of not only my struggles, but also my resiliency.

In this letter, I wrote that I hoped my future self would be compassionate and kind to herself; I hoped she would be living life in the present moment and finding pleasure in the things she loved. Infertility is not only isolating, but it's also completely defeating since you feel that there is no one else to blame except yourself.

Loving yourself and your body can be a real challenge. I had always been pretty confident and for the most part happy with myself; I didn't want infertility to strip me of this, and at times I felt that's exactly what it was doing.

I knew this game of infertility would come down to mindset and mental toughness, and I wanted to be as strong as possible so I could handle anything that came my way.

# 6

# *LAUREN: GREEK ODYSSEY*

After probably ten phone calls, twenty-five emails, and a call to my doctor, I finally got back on the IVF schedule three weeks later. Phew! I suddenly felt calm. Schedule in place, check. Round 2 is now a go, check. You see, what put me over the edge was not having a game plan in place. If I had a schedule, I was then able to focus on the next task and start chipping away at my to-do list. This was how I dealt with the stress of it all. Order and anger.

Round 2 went a little bit better than my first IVF. After the required two-week wait, my initial hCG levels came back at 110, a decent number. It was good, but it definitely wasn't completely reassuring. Typically, anything between 100 and 200 was a good sign, but ideally I was looking for levels over 200 to feel like I was in the "safe" zone.

"Wahoo-ewww," I said to my doctor when she gave me the news. "110," I groaned. "Can you please tell me what I am doing wrong because I feel like someone is playing a sick joke on me all over again."

Unfortunately/fortunately, Mackey and I were scheduled to head to Greece for vacation the very next day. We weren't about to cancel our trip, so my doctor came up with a plan: we would get my levels tested in Greece and have them sent back to his office.

"Sounds easy enough," I said, not thinking about the logistics of where and when I would be able to do this.

"Oh, and don't forget," he casually told me, "you are technically pregnant, so avoid the sun, don't drink alcohol, and remember, no soft cheeses."

A single tear rolled down my cheek as my romantic notions of enjoying wine, sun, and feta evaporated. He had basically negated the reasons we booked the trip in the first place. Nonetheless, I was pregnant! Or somewhat pregnant. We stuck to the plan, and the three of us (yes, I was now counting my two-week-old embie as a person) set off for Santorini, Greece.

As we touched down on one of the most beautiful islands in the world, our entire ten-day vacation ahead of us, my spirits were flying high. We were staying in a quaint little hotel with glorious views of the Aegean Sea and the caldera, Santorini's famous large volcanic crater. I pinched myself, knowing how fortunate I was to be in such a jaw-dropping, gorgeous destination. The bright-white, cave-like homes and azure-domed churches were dazzling. Small alleyways wrapped around the island, almost beckoning visitors to get lost in their history.

From the terrace of our hotel, we were able to enjoy 180-degree views of the breathtaking ocean. We felt like we were at the end of the world. Each morning started out with breakfast delivered to our terrace, a friendly reminder that leisurely sipping coffee with a million-dollar view is the greatest way to start a day.

I remembered having a moment of pure and utter bliss while sitting outside, looking over the ocean on our third day. I was pregnant, I was madly in love with my husband in this beautiful place, and life was perfect. The sun was shining through my soul, and I had this burst of happiness that radiated throughout my entire body. I will never forget that moment.

---

Day 5 of vacation came and I had to get my bloodwork done to see if my hCG levels had doubled. My fertility clinic had found a doctor who lived in the middle of the island who could take my blood samples. Mackey and I hailed a cab and set off on a thirty-minute ride. As we pulled up to the destination, I questioned the driver. "Hospital?"

We were in front of an apartment building, and I did not see one red cross sign anywhere indicating a hospital. The driver looked at me and shrugged.

"I knew I should have brushed up on my Greek before this," I said to Mackey as we exited the cab. Reluctantly we knocked on the door of the address given, and a small man in a pleated vest and glasses hurried us in the door. He then began to draw my blood in his living room. Awkward? Sure was. I silently berated myself for agreeing to get tested while on vacation, and not simply waiting until I got home.

The doctor took three vials of blood, then sent us on our way, telling us that he would send the results to our hotel. I felt like I was in the *Twilight Zone*. Why the hell was I putting myself through this while in paradise? Why didn't I just firmly tell my doctor, no? That I would wait till I got home to take another test? IVF continued to rule my life.

After two days of anxiously waiting for some kind of message, I got a call from the front desk. Finally, they had received a letter for us. We ran down to the lobby and with shaking hands ripped open the envelope.

"It's in Greek," I yelled to Mack, trying to decipher what all of the letters and symbols meant. After studying it for twenty minutes, we still could not figure out what the results were. We saw a very nice Greek couple lounging by the bar.

"Come on, let's go ask them to interpret it for us," said Mackey, knowing we needed the locals on this one. They spoke very little English but after many hand motions and broken Greek/English, we relayed that we needed to know if the letter said pregnant, or no.

After about a minute of scanning, the woman looked up at me sadly and said, "No pregnant."

The lovely islands of Greece quickly lost their luster, and I was ready to come home. How is it that I could be in the most gorgeous place on earth, on a trip of a lifetime with my wonderful husband, and IVF continued to rip me at the seams?

It ended up being an early-stage miscarriage. My hCG levels never reached higher than 120. Unlike the previous ectopic pregnancy, the fertilized embryo had made it into my uterus, but it failed to "stick" despite my lining being "plush" at the start of the cycle. Optimal uterine lining is generally anything above 8 mm and mine had topped out around 6 mm on my first round. Yet, this cycle I started with a 10 mm lining, which gave me hope. But, apparently, it wasn't sticky enough.

Oh hell! How many roadblocks would I have to face? I was beginning to seriously FREAK OUT, especially because it seemed I had done everything right this time. All my levels and numbers and temperatures and whatever else they were measuring had been perfect. Why wasn't it working? Mackey and I had come to learn that this is what is truly infuriating about IVF success or failure. It can sometimes be random and nonsensical. You begin to question, "If everything was perfect this round, how can I do anything more to change the outcome next time?" And sadly you realize that there is nothing you can do. You just have to keep on keeping on.

# 7

# LACEY: TAKING CONTROL

After the uterine balloon saga, I was ready for a change: Change of scenery, change of doctors, change of monotonous protocols. I was ready to take matters into my own hands and get some answers once and for all. And so, the do-er in me got to work.

I started to research the hell out of infertility, and over the course of two months, I visited six different doctors in three states. I did my homework and was determined to get in to see the top infertility doctors on the East Coast.

After four consultations with Baltimore and DC specialists, I finally scored a much sought-after appointment with a renowned fertility specialist, Dr. R, in New York City. My mom wanted to go with me; the nurse in her wanted answers, and she was ready to drill the best of the best with questions galore.

After we waited six weeks for this appointment, the day finally came. On a cold and dreary winter morning as we raced up Park Avenue on the East Side of Manhattan, I was filled with enormous hope and promise. Today was the day that we would finally get to meet the famous Dr. R. I felt like I was heading to meet the Dalai Lama himself. This man treated many famous women, and, in my eyes, he held the key to my having babies.

With so many thoughts racing through my head, I nervously reminded my mom how I wanted her to behave during this coveted appointment of limited time. "Mom," I began, "please let him do the talking. Remember he is a serious, no-nonsense type of man. Please don't ask a million questions like you always do. Just sit there and take in all his wisdom."

I quickly added, "And, Mom, thank you for paying for this appointment and coming up to NYC with me. What in the world would I do without you?" Because in truth, my greatest hope was to be like her one day—the ever-present mom who would do anything in the world for her children.

As we entered the enormous skyscraper, I was giddy with excitement. From the stunning marble lobby to the gorgeous views of Manhattan, I was convinced that this place would provide the answers to my problems. The pristine office felt like a spa—a huge upgrade from the shabbier, mediocre medical offices where I had spent so much time the previous years. This visit marked my fourth doctor consultation, in three states, and I was convinced that my time had come. I was firmly optimistic.

After checking in, we sat quietly in the waiting room, eyeing all the other patients. I felt my heart beating out of my chest. We were both so nervous that we didn't exchange a word. I attempted to read *Us Weekly* as we sat there, always on the lookout for another infertile celebrity who might have undergone IVF or even surrogacy. After all, those were my people.

Eventually I heard the words I had been waiting for: "Lacey O'Neil, you can come back now." Mom and I rose. I grabbed my tote, filled to the brim with 300 pages of past medical records, and we made our way back to Dr. R's office.

Meeting Dr. R felt like meeting an A-list celebrity. And it seemed he had the same opinion of himself. He barely shook our hands and got right down to business. Apparently small talk would have been a waste of his precious time. I gave him my five-minute pitch on why I was there, a summary I had perfected at this point, and my not-so-brief medical history. He then combed through my hundreds of papers while we sat in miserable silence, terrified of what he might conclude.

When he was done, he told me what every other doctor had told me—looks like unexplained amenorrhea. Are you FUCKING kidding me? Did I just wait what felt like a lifetime and then drag my ass (and my mom's) up to NYC for this diagnosis? Yes, I know what I have, but HOW THE HELL DO I FIX IT? In addition to having three failed IVFs and a balloon inserted in my uterus, I had tried everything else under the sun: gaining weight, not exercising, three consecutive years of weekly acupuncture, mindfulness workshops, no drinking, eating womb comforting and warming foods.

You name it, I'd tried it. And guess what, NONE of it worked. Dr. R. was supposed to be the best, but he had no insight for me. NONE. And on top of that, his arrogant manner was intimidating and unsettling.

It was in this meeting that I first mentioned the word *surrogacy* out loud, since one of his famous patients had recently had children via a surrogate. It terrified me to even try to wrap my head around having to think about surrogacy as an option. But I only had one shot with him, so I put on my big girl pants and asked the question: Did he think surrogacy was in my future?

He said it could be a possibility, but that I wasn't there yet. Leaving this appointment, I felt incredibly beaten down and no closer to getting the answers that I so desperately craved.

# GOING LOCAL

After we left the appointment, we popped into the nearest deli for a turkey sandwich before hitting the road and heading back to Maryland. I had to fuel up and have a clear mind because I had work to do. And can you guess what I did on that three-hour drive home to Annapolis? I researched the crap out of the best fertility clinics and doctors in my area, devouring everything I could find on the internet. I called a few clinics on the way home and booked two appointments for the following week, one in DC and one at Shady Grove in Annapolis. I was not about to give up this fight.

As luck would have it, the following Monday, I had a meeting with a highly regarded fertility specialist, Dr. Mottla, at Shady Grove in Annapolis. Not only did he accept my insurance (a big piece of the puzzle), but I would soon come to realize that he was the doctor I had been waiting for all along.

Dr. Mottla was the one. He was the doctor who transformed my life and left an indelible impact on me. His bedside manner was genuine and kind, and he had an exceptional ability to connect with people. Dr. Mottla was caring and had a brilliant brain. He perfectly balanced his toughness and tenderness.

From the outset, I knew that he was the doctor I had been seeking for my entire journey. He was the antithesis of Dr. R. Dr. Mottla gave me his complete attention and time. He comprehended my desire to continuously work toward my goal of having a child, but he also recognized the value of taking our time and ensuring that we made the correct choices for my treatment.

Working with Dr. Mottla proved to be the mental, physical, and emotional support that I needed. He possessed all the qualities I was looking for in a doctor, and I was thrilled to be receiving treatment at a state-of-the-art clinic.

Unfortunately, the first six months of treatment with Dr. Mottla were much like the previous two years. I underwent a couple of fresh egg retrievals resulting in multiple fertilized embryos, but when it came time for transfers, I still faced the same significant challenge: my thin lining.

Dr. Mottla was straightforward in expressing his concern about my uterine lining. While it didn't appear to be visibly scarred, he was worried about residual damage from the balloon procedure. Building a thick lining was likely to remain a challenge. We eventually concluded that no amount of estrogen and progesterone could ever help get my uterus in prime condition. Every transfer was met with high hopes and enormous expectations, only to be disappointed by my measly, little, paper-thin lining. To this day, the term *thin lining* haunts me in my dreams. We continued to do transfers each time, but they never resulted in a pregnancy. It seemed that my body was incapable of holding on to what I so desperately yearned for.

# DAY OF RECKONING

After experiencing eight failed embryo transfers, the emotional toll of infertility had left me feeling completely depleted. The mere thought of the number nine was overwhelming, and the feeling of burnout was like nothing I had ever experienced before. Even completing a marathon could not compare to the extent of the emotional exhaustion. The only consolation was reading about Celine Dion's sixth failed IVF cycle, which provided a sense of connection, but I knew that I could not reach out to her for support.

By June of 2010 we had come to a crossroads so we scheduled a meeting with Dr. Mottla to discuss our next steps. When Ben and I arrived at his office, the hope that we had been holding onto began to dissipate. However, Dr. Mottla's warm smile and greeting immediately put us at ease, reminding us that we were in capable hands. We viewed Dr. Mottla as more of a caring father figure than just our fertility doctor, which provided a comforting sense of trust since he was in charge of our future decisions.

As the warm summer sun shone through the expansive windows in the doctor's office, I felt like this might be a turning point, the glistening rays sending hope directly to me. Ben must have felt the same way because he leaned over and kissed my head.

We found our seats in the all-too-familiar chairs of his office and exchanged pleasantries about the weather at the beach and the frustrating back-up at the Chesapeake Bay Bridge. My mind was doing flips. Is there a fast-forward button? *Kill the small talk and cut to the chase,* I thought to myself as I crossed my legs and shook my ankle impatiently. I was anxious to understand more about our most recent failed cycle, as if there could really be answers at this point. It all seemed impossible to keep doing the same thing over and over. If I was being honest with myself, I wasn't so sure I had a ninth transfer in me. Scary to admit, but my hope to carry a baby was rapidly fading.

Dr. Mottla went on to discuss the favorable stimulation, oocyte retrieval, fertilization, and excellent quality of embryo development I had with the most recent single embryo transfer. He explained how during the last round he extended the time frame to build up and prepare my uterine lining even more. While it appeared adequate, it was still suboptimal. My mind stopped. Freezing rain during the Raven's playoff game is suboptimal. Failing this latest cycle of IVF wasn't suboptimal. It was cataclysmic. Isn't there any way to fix it? Any way to make it optimal? For God's sake, in this day and age, why can't we figure this out?

My brain was swimming. What was Dr. Mottla saying? I did not give a shit about the details. I just wanted to know the bottom line. And there it was. "Lacey and Ben," he said kindly, "it's time to discuss other options for having a baby."

Other options? Did he actually just say that? Hearing the words aloud sucked the air right out of my lungs. I clutched my throat trying to remember how to breathe. Maybe I was dreaming? Please, Lacey, wake up! Ben's eyes pooled with tears as he squeezed my hand and put on a brave face.

He would later tell me that the pain he felt for me at that moment was the most helpless he'd ever felt in his whole life. If you have ever watched someone suffer and not be able to help them, you know how Ben felt. Not only were his own dreams of having a family crumbling before his eyes, but his no-hill-is-too-big-go-getter wife was disintegrating into ashes, and he was powerless.

The anxiety that filled me moments before turned to dread and sadness. Is a doctor really telling me that the likelihood of me ever being able to carry a baby is slim to none? Soul crushing is putting it lightly. The pit in my stomach was the size of a basketball. Once the words were out in the open, I felt a tightness in my throat and my heart was rapidly thumping. *Don't cry, Lace, bite your cheek, stay strong, hold it together, please,* I begged myself.

My body went boneless at that moment. Later when I got home and was in the shower, I was able to let it all out. I had that uncontrollable crying fit where you turn into a puddle. The ugly cry. You have probably been there—snot dripping uncontrollably from your nose, thick spit hanging from your lips. Hunched over and shaking uncontrollably. Absolute desperation as I fell to the shower floor. I still feel my heart clench in my chest just recalling that moment. But here was the deal: I needed to face the music, and I wanted to put on a brave face for everyone else.

Reality check: My body cannot have a baby. Breathe. Breathe. Plan C. Surrogacy or adoption. Breathe. I would be lying if I said that I did not have that victim mentality. I sure did. Why could everyone else have a freaking baby and not me? What did I do wrong? I felt I had completely failed not only myself, but everyone I love.

After more than three years and eight failed attempts, my default setting/growth mindset was impaired beyond repair and I was in complete despair. All those years of Catholic schooling taught me that having a family was the next natural step after marriage. But more than that, I yearned for a baby. And yet it seemed my body was broken. I felt that to my core. No amount of medicine or surgeries were going to fix it. I needed a miracle. *Hello, God? Can you hear me?*

Ben knew I was at the end of my rope with IVF and needed a new direction. I tried to switch gears over the next few days. Maybe this could be a good thing? We began the hard topics of discussion: adoption and surrogacy. We realized that what we wanted most in this world was a baby, and if we must try other options to get our baby, then so be it.

*Lacey,* I thought to myself, *stop wallowing in the woe-is-me and turn on that machine mindset that has carried you this far in life. Goodbye, victim mentality. Eyes on the prize and keep moving in that direction.*

I took a day or two to mourn the baby that I would never carry, and then I decided that it was time to forge ahead and gain back my strength. Ben and I decided that we would first explore surrogacy. I was already familiar with the IVF process, which surrogacy also entailed, and I actually felt comfortable with the notion of using another woman's uterus to provide a stable environment for my baby to grow. For some reason, I feel guilty saying it, but I also wanted a child that was biologically ours if that was a possibility. We were fortunate enough financially to be able to afford it. We may have had to empty our savings, but we could do it. I did not know a soul on earth who had ever used a surrogate, but I was having my own goddamn family, come hell or high water.

# 8

# LAUREN: GAME ON

After returning from Greece, I was anxious to start another IVF round. I had felt the exhilaration of a positive test and felt like my luck was going to turn. I was told that we couldn't start another cycle until my hormone levels came back down, an indication that my body had naturally expelled the pregnancy. I waited and waited, but my levels weren't dropping, and the constant back and forth to the doctor's office to test my levels was infuriating. Why weren't these levels coming down?

Again, the waiting, for me, was one of the hardest things I had to face. After about three weeks, my doctor told me that I would have to have a D&C since my body was not responding naturally to the miscarriage. Add this to the list of procedures that I would have to endure. And not only that, I would have to take another three days off work.

At the time, I was working on the trading floor of a brokerage house, and all the personal time off was starting to look suspicious. When you are working as a trader, you are meant to be at your desk at all times. You eat lunch at your desk, and if you need to hit the loo, you must inform your backup that you'll be off for five minutes.

There was no hiding my new IVF gig. Looks like I was going to have an awkward convo with the boss man about my infertility. And not only that, I knew my constant whereabouts would be questioned by all of my coworkers (basically all men), and everyone on the entire trading floor would soon come to know that I was infertile. Talk about depressing.

"Angel, it looks like I am going to be taking some days off here and there and will also be out some mornings and afternoons for doctors' appointments. Female stuff," I explained to my boss of ten years.

And that was pretty much all that needed to be said. He turned bright red and replied, "Yeah, yeah, all good, Laur. Whatever you need." He quickly jumped up and opened the door to his office for me. He wanted out of this convo just as much as I did.

I went through three more IVF cycles within the next nine months, and each one ended in failure. Not only was I not going to be one of those damn lucky first timers, I couldn't even score after five attempts. So you may wonder, what is it like going through so many cycles and never getting pregnant? It is the very definition of demoralizing. It sucks the breath out of you and makes you question life as you know it.

Mackey and I felt completely beaten down at this point, but what was our alternative? We weren't ready to give up yet, but I started to seriously question the process. After all, isn't the definition of crazy doing the same thing over and over again and expecting a different outcome?

Let's also talk about the financial toll this was taking on us. We had already blown through our lifetime max amount of infertility benefits through my insurance and were now paying out of pocket for each cycle. I remember the day that we found out that round number 5 was a bust. Mackey came home looking miserable.

"Laur, we can't keep going on like this. We are going to go broke if we continue at this rate. This is breaking us physically, emotionally, and financially."

"I know," I sobbed, "the logical side of me says that this needs to end. But I can't give up for some sick reason." I wanted a baby so badly it made my insides ache.

Thankfully both Mackey and I had good-paying jobs with decent income. We both also still had our First Communion money saved from when we were eight years old. Yes, you could say we are savers. Each of us admits that one of our favorite childhood pastimes was heading to the community bank to deposit our babysitting and lawn mowing money. The universe knew that we were going to need it.

But we did not have endless funds and the financial responsibility was starting to suffocate us. I cannot imagine how some couples do it. We were the lucky ones. While it was hard, it was possible for us to continue on, cycle after cycle. Other people literally have to use their life savings on one or two cycles. If those do not work, they have nowhere to turn. I counted my blessings, for sure, that we were even financially able to continue treatments, but it still felt like physical and emotional torture.

Regardless of how many rounds you go through, it never gets easier, and the failures only get worse. We headed into cycle 6 with absolutely no expectations and little to no hope. I had convinced myself that the DINK lifestyle was actually going to be a fabulous life of good wine, gourmet food, and traveling to remote countries.

This time, we had six decent embryos that fertilized after the retrieval. We were adamant about putting two embryos in— double the chances, right? And twins would be amazing! Hell, I wanted to put all six in, let's have an entire litter.

We were now under the care of Lacey's doctor, Dr. Mottla, at Shady Grove Fertility in Annapolis. Dr. Mottla sat us down before the transfer and said that he wanted to discuss the risks of multiple pregnancies.

"Guys, I need you both to understand the risks of multiple pregnancies. They are far higher than that of a singleton pregnancy. The chance of going into preterm labor and/or having complications throughout the pregnancy are far greater," he explained.

I remember this day and this moment so vividly. Sitting in his office, Mackey to the left of me, and both of us nodding our heads, acting like we were completely aware of what he was telling us. Yes, I was listening to him, but I wasn't actually "listening" to his advice. I knew what I wanted and I believed that putting two embryos in, just as we had done in all of our other cycles, was what we needed to do. And that is what we did, despite his warnings.

The transfer went smoothly and after the ten-day wait, I got my hCG level—it was 305. Holy shite! 305! Not only was it high, but it was twin-level high! And the numbers continued to double.

We went in for our first ultrasound with high hopes, coupled with a ton of anxiety, as always. The minute Dr. Mottla started the ultrasound, I stopped breathing. I would not/could not breathe as they were scanning my uterus looking for those embryos. It seemed to take an eternity as he carefully stared at the monitor, and I carefully stared at the doctor to watch his expression. I couldn't stand that worried look—his furrowed brow as if he was trying to find a needle in a haystack.

I prayed, *Dr. Mottla, please don't let me down. For the love of God find at least one embryo.* And indeed he did find one. And then another.

"Looks like two healthy embryos in there guys," he said, looking just as happy as we were feeling. The joy I felt was like a tidal wave washing over me, taking my breath away.

Mackey and I were stunned, ecstatic, overjoyed. We skipped out of the office, floating on air, staring numbly at one another.

Fifteen minutes later, the worry set it. What if something goes wrong? What if I start to bleed? What if I miscarry? I had six more weeks until I was twelve weeks' gestation, at which point I would be out of the dreaded first trimester when most miscarriages occur. Oh, how the doubt and fear so quickly weaseled their way in and found a fertile home. *When did I become such a negative person,* I thought. I have always been the person who believes good things will happen to her. Hell, I believe that I will get that primo parking space directly out front every time, and damned if it doesn't happen. I couldn't stand the negative thoughts that kept popping up in my head. It was like whack-a-mole. Subdue the fear of one bad outcome and up would pop another.

"Okay, so I am so excited, but maybe I should just go home and lie down for the next six weeks?" I told Mackey, believing that if I didn't move too much, the babies wouldn't jiggle their way out of me.

This hamster wheel of failed IVFs and miscarriages had left me weary and broken down. I tried to let myself really open up to the fact that I was pregnant with twins and let myself bask in this joy. A week went by and all was well—still not feeling any signs of pregnancy, but I was chugging along. And then we entered week 8 and I started to bleed. My world came crashing down while I sat in the bathroom at work, staring at the blood in the toilet. I quickly called Mackey, who tried to calm me down, but who, I could tell, was as crushed as I was.

I frantically called Dr. Mottla who was not in the office but said he could see me the next day if I'd like. Yes, please. He was lucky I wasn't showing up at his front doorstep at that very moment. I continued to have spotting throughout the day and night. I also continued to prepare myself for the worst—that I had lost the pregnancies, just as Lacey had done. This was my new defense tactic and mantra: prepare for the worst. Fear was my new outlook.

The drive to the Shady Grove office in Bethesda the next morning took an hour. Neither of us said a word. I was too nervous to even pretend to act normally at this point. After we checked in at the front desk, we were quickly called back to the office, and Dr. Mottla solemnly greeted us as he entered the room. We immediately got down to business with the ultrasound wand.

On cue, I stopped breathing. Time stood still. And then I saw them, two little bleeping amoebas. They were still there! They had stuck, and they had little beating hearts! We were all crying and shouting and high-fiving. Wow, talk about a turn of emotions; I just went from, "I'd like to throw myself off a cliff" to "Praise be, I am actually preggers with twins!" Nap, please.

Dr. Mottla told us that there can be a lot of blood in pregnancies (hmm, it would have been helpful to have known that), especially twin pregnancies, and I could continue to have this spotting for the rest of my first trimester. He also saw a small hematoma in my uterus, which can be normal. A hematoma forms when blood pools in tissue instead of in the blood vessels, causing vaginal bleeding. All of this sounded very scary, but Dr. Mottla assured us that these hematomas usually absorb themselves and do not interfere with pregnancy.

I was told to rest and take it easy for the next few weeks. If I had to sit on my ass for the next ten months, bring it on (and this is coming from someone who can't go a day without getting some form of sweat in).

For the next four weeks I basically sat around, ate whatever I could get my hands on, and continued to spot and worry. Mostly worry. Good times, people, good times. I put myself in a teeny-weeny IVF bubble and could barely answer a phone call or participate in the outside world because, for the life of me, I couldn't think about anything else.

My pregnancy consumed me and overtook my life. The only time I felt safe was when I was at work and had the distraction of the trading floor and a roomful of men yelling at one another. The very thought of having to go to the bathroom put the fear of God in me. Would there be blood, and if so, how much? My water consumption went down to a few sips a day and I started to lie with my legs twined together at my thighs. Yes, I thought I could hold them in there. Pure and utter agony.

I finally made it to week 13, the mecca of safe harbor pregnancies, where I was told my chances of miscarriage had drastically reduced. I could breathe again. I could tell people why I had jumped off the face of the earth for what seemed to be years now. If I was a social media person, which I'm not, I'm pretty sure my post could have been: "Update: I have been going through IVF and my life has sucked, and I secretly hated you all for getting pregnant so easily, and I was dying inside, but guess what, I am having two bambinos now, and my world is right again!"

# 9

# LACEY: OUR SURROGATE SAGA

Once we decided to explore the option of surrogacy, I wasted no time in learning everything possible about this process and how it works. I made it my mission to find the best surrogate out there.

We met with Dr. Mottla two weeks later, and he explained how fortunate we were that one of the best surrogacy centers in the United States was in Annapolis, only two miles away from where we were presently sitting. He said he had many patients fly in from all over the world to work simultaneously with him and the Center for Surrogacy Parenting, commonly referred to as CSP.

Was he telling me that this California-based agency seriously has their one and only East Coast office in Annapolis, within walking distance of my house? A glimmer of hope ignited inside me. It finally felt like the universe was working in our favor.

Dr. Mottla explained the details of using a gestational carrier, which is the formal name for a surrogate. He discussed the role of agencies, the initial steps to take, the significant financial

71

obligations, the various requirements for the surrogate, the mandatory psychological evaluations for everyone involved, and the diverse state laws related to surrogacy. With so much information to absorb, it was overwhelming to remember everything.

Surrogacy laws can be complex, so Dr. Mottla advised us to hire a lawyer as a priority. Luckily, we knew a family friend who was a lawyer with vast experience in this field. Peggy Ricely, as I knew her from the days when I babysat her three young children, was one of the more knowledgeable lawyers in the field of surrogacy and adoption. When I told Dr. Mottla that we were working with Peggy, or Margaret Swain as she goes by for professional purposes, his eyes lit up. He knew her very well and had worked with her on numerous cases in the past. He assured us we were in some of the best hands possible.

As soon as we started researching surrogacy, I had a realization. Having a baby wasn't about me. Rather, it was about creating a family with Ben and having a baby to love. If this was the first selfless act that I must do as a mother, giving up control of the process and letting my baby grow inside another woman, then so be it. Ego checked at the door, no wallowing or self-pity from this point forward. I had to keep my mind focused on being grateful for this process and the gift of life. Although I was ready to move forward with surrogacy, deep down inside my soul I still had a glimmer of hope that someday I might be able to carry a baby myself.

As we were leaving the doctor's office, I shared my feelings with Dr. Mottla. "Dr. M, someday, someway, somehow, I truly believe I will still carry my own baby," I told him. Dr. Mottla's response was realistic but heartwarming. "Lacey," he said, "I love your optimism and determination. If I thought that was at all possible, I would not have approved you for surrogacy. But I truly hope that you prove me wrong one day and do have that forty-year-old whoops baby. I would welcome that conversation. And after all," he concluded, "Miracles do happen."

After we left the office, Ben and I kissed each other goodbye, got into our cars, and headed our separate ways to work. On my thirty-minute drive, I capitalized on my free time and set up an appointment with Peggy, the surrogacy lawyer, for Wednesday of that week. Before I even pulled into my parking space, I had called the Center for Surrogate Parenting and set up an appointment with them as well. I spent the rest of the day pretending to work, but instead, I read everything I could on the topic of surrogacy. I wanted to soak up every precious bit of information on the subject. I couldn't get enough. What did people in my situation in the past do without the internet?

Fast-forward two days to our Wednesday meeting with Peggy. It was a lovely, spring May day as we entered her Towson office. I was incredibly nervous for this meeting, scared of what she would tell us. Even though I was onboard with moving forward, it was a lot to take in.

Peggy was lovely as always, welcoming us with her warm smile. She provided us with comprehensive information on the two options that were available to us; she wanted to arm us with as much knowledge as possible before making a final decision. As Peggy explained the adoption process, I couldn't help but feel empathy for anyone who has gone through it. It seemed like such a difficult and emotionally taxing process. I thought about my nephew, Nicholas, who was adopted, and I was inspired by the love and determination his parents showed in their journey to adopt him. While we were still considering adoption as an option, Ben and I ultimately decided that surrogacy would be our first choice.

Once we decided to use our own embryos and proceed with a gestational carrier, our next step was to meet with the CSP that Friday. The meeting was highly informative and helpful in walking us through the entire process, detailing it from beginning to end. But I was having a tough time wrapping my head around the exorbitant cost of surrogacy. I am sorry, did you say $100,000 for a baby? We were a couple who both worked full-time as professionals but whether we could afford it or not, that is a lot of damn money! What really got me was that we had to pay the agency a fee of $30,000 just to pair us with a gestational surrogate. From there we would pay prenatal fees and a considerable sum to the carrier herself. And on top of this, most of their carriers would likely be living in different states.

After the meeting, I was having a tough time wrapping my head around this process and the agency's role in it. I wasn't on board with this yet. Maybe I was becoming more okay with not being able to carry my own baby, but one thing I was not comfortable with was my baby being born all the way across the freaking United States.

There must be a closer, less expensive, and better alternative. I daydreamed about attending every prenatal appointment and doing every little thing that a mom does, short of carrying the child, throughout the pregnancy. Was I supposed to fly to California for every little check-up? I still had some research to do. I needed to feel comfortable with how this process unfolded and how we were spending our life savings.

After some serious thought, I decided that I would take on the task of finding a gestational carrier myself. My plan was to try it on my own for a few months, and if I wasn't successful, then we would return to the Center for Surrogate Parenting for assistance. I was eager to channel my energy and passion into building our family, and I believed that finding the right match for us was something that I could accomplish. However, I needed to persuade Ben to agree with this approach. He was a bit hesitant and felt that it would be safer to empty our savings account and go with CSP right away. Ben knew me well and was aware of my determination and frugality (I like to think I am smart with my money, not cheap, there is a difference!). And so, I began a new journey—this time to find the perfect baby mama.

# *THE SEARCH*

For the next few months, I did the bare minimum of my professional work and spent eight hours a day online. My mission was to reach out to as many people as possible and connect with potential gestational carriers (GCs) on websites that catered to intended parents (IPs) looking for surrogates. I searched for keywords like *East Coast*, *Mid Atlantic*, and *Maryland* to narrow my search. Even though my search was all-consuming, I kept it a secret from my family, friends, and coworkers. I felt embarrassed and couldn't figure out how to tell them about my new venture.

I tried to keep my excitement in check when meeting some of these surrogates online, because—as Peggy had warned me—you need to be incredibly careful and cautious as there are scammers who prowl these sites in hopes of stealing money from desperate people. And trust me, people in my situation are desperate, I can tell you from experience. In fact, this was the most desperate and vulnerable period of my life.

Chat rooms became my specialty, and my obsession. After about three months of searching, I met (online, of course) the first candidate who would be interested in carrying my baby. Her name was Danielle, and she was from Pittsburgh—only a three-hour drive away. I loved my conversations with Danielle, who was a third-time surrogate and had three children of her own. She was happily married and from our conversations she seemed very grounded with sincere intentions. We clicked right away, and she even sent me pictures of her children. She told me that pregnancy was easy and enjoyable for her, and she loved the idea of providing a miracle for people like me.

Danielle was perfect. I'd hit the jackpot! Thank you, God. But would Dr. Mottla approve her? This would be Danielle's seventh pregnancy, and I knew Dr. Mottla was adamant on a six-pregnancy maximum for surrogates. Shady Grove Fertility Center, where Dr.

Mottla practiced, had strict rules, and I had to believe that adhering to them was for good reason and in our best interest. And so, a few days later, as I feared, Dr. Mottla crushed my hope of having Danielle in my life. I felt as if my heart was shattered into a million pieces. Time to start my search over. We were back to zero.

## EUREKA!

It was late August 2010, and my sole mission in life was to find my angel. So back to chat rooms I went.

One site which I frequented was www.surromomsonline.com, an online community and forum for both intended parents and gestational carriers. By the grace of God, one day I came across an ad looking for an intended couple to pair with a ready and willing GC. And guess what? This GC was right here in Maryland, my home state. I couldn't believe my eyes. Was this for freaking real?

My fingers could not type a response fast enough, and within minutes I received a response with her "e-résumé," which gave her background, location, familial and medical history, and a brief description of her intentions for being a carrier. Was this too good to be true or simply the universe finally aligning? Not only did this woman live in Maryland, but she was also Catholic, happily married, and had completed her family, with three children of her own. And damn it if she didn't go to an ob-gyn at Greater Baltimore Medical Center, where my mom had worked as a nurse for over thirty years and the same hospital where I had been born.

Little did I know at the time, but this woman was contractually represented by an agency. Her agency oversaw finding the perfect family for her to match. I would need to pay $7,000 to the agency, who would help us enter a contract. Looking back on it now, this seems crazy to me. I had found her on my *own*. But I was desperate and while this was a considerable sum of money, it was certainly less than the $30,000 that CSP charged. And so, the next step was to meet my living angel, Becky.

## START HERE

As you can imagine, our first meeting was filled with much anticipation and lots of nerves. Can you actually imagine meeting a stranger who plans to carry your child inside her? It's a lot to grasp.

We met at Anne Arundel Medical Center, where we all had to separately meet with a psychologist to confirm that we were each of sound mind before proceeding. Meeting Becky and her husband, Greg, for the first time felt surreal. I could not help but give this stranger a huge hug; a handshake would not have sufficed. I embraced her and wanted to hold on for dear life. After those first meetings with the psychologist, we spent time over dinner getting to know each other.

Luckily, Ben and I hit it off with Becky and Greg immediately. We learned a lot about their kids, their life in Baltimore, their jobs, their family and friends, and eventually what brought them to the surrogacy process. Put simply, they are the salt of the earth and amazing human beings.

---

It takes a pair of strikingly selfless and caring people to agree to do this. Not only was Becky putting her body through a considerable amount of stress (plus she had already had two C-sections and would require another one for this birth), but a lot fell on Greg as well. He would have to provide the emotional support that every GC needs, as well as physical support as she got further along in the pregnancy. He would have to care for their three young kids should she need to go on bed rest and once she was in the hospital for the birth as well as for her recovery. This was a joint decision, and they were both fully on board.

Becky and I stayed connected over the next month as we prepared to undergo our first transfer. Ben and I had five frozen embryos, two of which we planned to use for the transfer. In November 2010, after getting her cycle in sync and taking the necessary hormones, Becky was finally ready for a transfer. We decided to put two embryos in, hoping that at least one would take. Walking out of the office after that first procedure was like walking along the most gorgeous beach at sunset, pure bliss. It was such a relief not to be the one going through it physically. Although the loss of control was a new feeling I needed to embrace, I was happy and hopeful, with a bit of nervous anticipation mixed in.

Up next was the dreaded two-week wait (TWW) to see if the transfer worked. This TWW was quite different, given that I could not squeeze my boobs constantly to see if they were sore, or try to figure out if I was craving one food over another, or feel for every little cramp and the possibility of implantation. This wait was in some ways much easier, especially given all the confidence that I had in Becky's womb and its ability to get pregnant.

When the day of Becky's blood test finally arrived, I was a bundle of nerves, biting off all my nails and downing forty-five gallons of coffee. I had gone through every emotion during the previous two weeks. It is mental torture whether you are the one experiencing it, or your GC is experiencing it. It took all my willpower not to constantly email her asking, "How are you feeling?" I clung to every word and reread every sentence that she wrote to me in her emails, always looking for some sort of sign that she was pregnant.

The day of her test seemed to drag on for hours and hours and around three that afternoon the nurse from Shady Grove called me. I knew from experience that this was not a good sign. Typically, when the result is positive, your nurse or doctor will call you immediately, usually mid to late morning, to share the good news. But the later in the afternoon it gets, the less promising the outcome. They save the worst calls for the end of the day, or so my crazy mind thought. And I was right.

After a brief pleasantry with the nurse, all I heard was the dreaded word: *negative.* "I'm sorry, Lacey, but the pregnancy blood test came back and it's negative." I was in shock. How could this happen? Becky wasn't pregnant. This was not how it was supposed to end. Despite feeling devastated myself, I knew I had to keep my composure and be there for Becky. She was taking it extremely hard and kept apologizing to me. I reassured her that it wasn't her fault and that there was no need for both of us to feel responsible. I wanted to shoulder the burden and spare her from feeling any worse. Only one of us needed to feel shitty and responsible. It's the least I can do. *Let me handle that,* I thought.

We ended our call and a wave of despair knocked into me. Shaking and shivering in devastation, I got into my car and sobbed. Sheer terror took over. My carrier couldn't get pregnant with our embryos. What the hell was I going to do? I had never contemplated that it might not work and that we would be no better off than where we started.

I was exhausted from these last few years, from putting on a brave face, from being optimistic, from hoping for the best, from finding something positive in this entire experience. I felt completely drained and unsure about how I was going to go on. How could I ever be happy again after this blow? The only person at all that I wanted to be around was Ben. Sobbing, I started my car and headed home to be with him.

Later that week, the first week of December 2010, Ben and I headed out on a date night to Harry Browne's, a charming, dimly lit speakeasy type bar in the heart of Annapolis. What should have been a cozy, pre-Christmas dinner date night felt lifeless, flat, and frankly depressing. We couldn't brave going out to see our friends, so we stuck together and planned outings just the two of us. Our topic of conversation steered toward "baby" as it always did. Frankly, was there anything else to even talk about? Not for me. It is the only thing I had come to care about.

Both of us come from close-knit, large families with whom we share every holiday. We alternate back and forth, trying to see each family equally year after year. This Christmas it was our turn to be in Baltimore with my family, the Aumillers. Christmas is by far my favorite holiday. I love when I get to stay at my parents' house and wake up in my old room and have Christmas with my siblings.

But this year I could not do it. I felt like a weak coward admitting it, but I could not face going to Christmas Eve mass, where we would see all of Baltimore, and the adorable families with young babies and kids dressed up in their green and red smocked dresses and blazers. I could not bear to see all the giddy children and families pack into pew after pew, while it is just the two of us again this year. It would have broken my heart even more if that were even possible.

"What's our option?" I asked Ben. Not thinking that we ever even had one. But we decided without delay that this Christmas was going to be about self-preservation. It was about us finding a little bit of happiness in whatever form that might be. I just could not face a family Christmas this year.

Were we actually entertaining the idea of no Christmas? Was that even a possibility? I had always been a good daughter and done what I was supposed to do, putting family first at every turn. I was shocked that I was willing to give up Christmas with the family that I adore and just let it come and go this year.

But Ben and I decided we had to do something that we both knew we would enjoy the most—travel. As I previously mentioned, after our twin miscarriage in 2009, we traveled to Napa wine country. After three hellish years of infertility and my eighth and final failed attempt at IVF, we took a fifth anniversary trip to Italy. So, on that freezing cold December evening, we decided that we would leave town for Christmas. We would rejuvenate and distract ourselves from our sorrows. Riviera Maya, Mexico, here we come! Tequila shots please. We were skipping Christmas!

# 10

# LAUREN: THE WAITING GAME

It seemed like years ago, not weeks, that Dr. Mottla had sat us down and told us all about the risks of multiple pregnancies. Those worries I had early on had mostly dissipated now that I was in my thirteenth week. I was one week into my second trimester and was ecstatic. Generally, about 80 percent of all miscarriages occur in the first trimester, and I was so damn happy to be out of that territory.

I am tall at 5 feet 8 inches, with a strong athletic build, and if anyone could carry twin pregnancies, it was me. Or so I thought. I had seen my sister-in-law, Jen, carry twins to thirty-eight weeks and deliver a 6 and 7 pounder. Of course, I would and could do the same.

I coasted through the next few weeks feeling great and decided that we should get away for the weekend to celebrate that I had made it through the first trimester. I booked a weekend at The Equinox in Vermont, an idyllic New England resort that would showcase the gorgeous fall foliage. At this point, I was thinking, could life get any better? I was absolutely floating on air and the weightlessness that I felt was a respite after years of worry and wondering.

The first day of the trip we went on a long hike through Vermont's beautiful Green Mountains, in awe of the natural beauty that was surrounding us. I got a lovely pregnancy massage at the spa, drifting in and out of a blissful semiconscious state and was gently awakened by my masseuse.

"Would you like me to bring you a warm cup of apple cider to enjoy by the stone fireplace?" she whispered in my ear. Um, pinch me now because this is heaven. A starring role in my own Lifetime movie.

We headed back to our room to get dressed for dinner, and Mackey decided to put the moves on me. To put it bluntly, Mackey is a horny toad. Like many men, Mackey particularly loves hotel sex. I knew I wasn't getting out of this one. Despite my newly formed belly and newfound tiredness, I indulged the hubs because I am a good wife. And because my boobs were so big, I thought at least one of us should be enjoying them.

After the deed was done, I went to the bathroom and immediately started screaming when I saw what was in the toilet. A thick bloody mucus was floating in the bowl. I thought my days of dreading what might happen when I went to the bathroom were long gone. In fact, I had just recently started using the toilet without first saying a Hail Mary.

But now I was in terror again. Whatever was in that toilet looked like it definitely needed to be inside me to protect the babies. Whatever I had just lost, I knew deep down I needed for a healthy pregnancy. What was that thing that people always talked about losing right before birth? A mucus plug of some sort?

I quickly started googling images and when I didn't like the answers I found there, I started calling people.

I frantically phoned my sister-in-law, Jen, my go-to for twin pregnancy-related questions and told her what had happened. She said that in all pregnancies, especially twin births, there was always going to be a lot of discharge. Like a ton of discharge. I then called my doctor's office, and the on-call nurse told me the same thing. She said that sex should not cause me to lose my mucus plug.

I started to calm down a bit and decided that all was well. I was going to enjoy myself and think positively. We went to a quaint little tavern in town that night for dinner and reveled in at least twelve different kinds of Vermont cheddar, among other treats. I got back to the room and plopped down like a whale on the bed, thanking God that we had gotten busy earlier in the night and Mackey wasn't going to get any ideas now. No one was laying a finger on this mama.

By morning, I still hadn't experienced any more discharge, yet I took the last two days of the vacation easy and didn't do too much physical activity. I was definitely worried, but I was feeling okay. I did not have any other symptoms, and with each hour, I became more and more relaxed.

We flew back to Annapolis Monday night. I was scheduled for an ultrasound the next morning before work. Mackey came with me as usual. After weighing in and heartbeat checks, the tech showed us back to the ultrasound room, and I jumped up, excited to see my two little embies. I hadn't exactly been nervous because, so far, everything had been fine. I wasn't bleeding or having additional discharge, and I had no cramps or contractions.

As with every ultrasound, the minute that wand entered, I immediately turned my attention to the face of the ultrasound specialist. I looked for the furrowed brow, a quick smile, or a confused expression. Nonchalant chattiness was always welcome, as that usually meant they liked what they were seeing.

I was getting "furrowed brow" coupled with "confused expression." There was no chatting, and there was definitely no smiling. It was utter silence and it lasted for a full two minutes. My heart was beating through my chest, and I was squeezing Mackey's hand till it turned purple.

"I'll be right back," said the nurse. At lightning speed, Dr. K, my ob-gyn, materialized in the room, took a quick look at the ultrasound, and told me to carefully make my way to his office. My nightmare had just begun.

# EMERGENT SITUATION

Dr. K told me that my cervix was fully dilated, and he would have to perform emergency cerclage surgery to prevent me going into labor right then and there.

"Wha whaattt . . . what are you saying?" I managed to yell out. "I could go into labor right now?" I was frantic.

Cerclage surgery involves placing one or two sutures around the cervical opening. To put it simply, the doctor sews up your cervix to prevent premature birth. Dr. K also told us that the surgery this late in the game, at twenty weeks' gestation with twins, results in only about a 20 percent fetus survival rate. Most cerclages are put in when a woman is twelve weeks pregnant, before the baby gets too big and the uterus is in danger of rupturing. I was twenty weeks and two days pregnant at this point.

Within minutes a nurse entered Dr. K's office with a wheelchair. Panic mode! I wasn't allowed to even walk down the corridor to the pre-op room? Little did I know, this would be the last day I would be on my feet for the next month. How could this be happening? How could I possibly endure more? Surely, I thought, I was finished with the hardship. Not fair. I concentrated on breathing and staying calm.

Ten minutes later, I was wheeled into the operating room and they began pre-op. I was so scared that I couldn't even speak. They told me I would be awake for the surgery because general anesthesia could be harmful to the babies. Mackey wasn't allowed in the room, so I was without my support team. The only sound I could hear was the babies' heartbeats coming through on the monitor. Dear Lord, I may physically witness the sound of my babies' beating hearts go silent if this surgery doesn't work.

The nurses began to strap my legs into stirrups, stretching them basically behind my head. It was undoubtedly the most vulnerable position possible. Imagine being in a happy baby yoga pose, naked with eight people staring at your vagina and ass. The room was dead silent as Dr. K carefully began placing the cerclage, basically stitching up my cervix. No one dared to utter a sound for fear that his hand might slip even the tiniest bit. All I could listen to and focus on was the heartbeat monitor.

After the longest fifteen minutes of my life, with barely a few breaths taken during that time (or so it seemed), Dr. K announced that the stitch was in, and the babies were okay for the moment. He explained that my cervical length, basically the amount of cervix that he was able to work with, was extremely small. The pressure of the babies would eventually weigh too heavily on the stitch, and I would be forced into early labor.

Imagine a bowling ball wrapped up in a wet paper towel and hanging on a hook. It would be only a matter of time before it broke through. Still, I let out a huge sigh of relief that the babies had made it through surgery. It was not until I got back into the recovery room that I realized the full extent of the situation. I was ready to go home, but the doctor said I would not be leaving. Not only would I not be leaving, I would not be getting out of bed for the foreseeable future.

I asked him, "If I get to thirty weeks, can I go home for the rest of the pregnancy?"

Dr. K looked at me as if I were crazy. "Lauren, you will be lucky if you make it to twenty-four weeks with these babies."

I was speechless. Twenty-four weeks of gestation was barely viable, the babies would have only a slim chance of surviving at twenty-four weeks when forty is the norm. Fear and helplessness engulfed me.

Later that day, I was wheeled into my new room in the high risk labor and delivery unit. This would be my room for the foreseeable future. It was a small room with beige walls and a set of windows looking out to the parking lot. A couch folded out to a single-sized bed for overnight guests.

Mackey took one look at that couch and said, "Well, looks like this is where I'll be laying my head for the foreseeable future." He stretched out, only to have his legs hang a good two feet off the end. I told him that he did not have to be spending the nights at the hospital with me to which he smiled, "I'm not staying for you. I'm staying for the room service breakfast obviously."

I stayed on bedrest for four weeks. Every minute of every day I looked for signs: water breaking, cramping, contractions. People came in to see me, but I didn't want company, I just wanted to focus on twenty-four weeks. Mackey did not leave my side, and Mom and Lacey visited daily, counting down the hours with me. I regularly recited a mantra chant to myself. "Twenty-four . . . viable . . . twenty-four . . . viable."

Those four weeks were filled with obsessions. The first one was food. Hospital meals are all you have, so I planned them meticulously, strategically ordering on a set schedule to make the days go by faster. For each meal, a patient was allowed to order one main dish, four sides, two desserts, and five drinks. Well damned if I didn't meet that quota with every meal. You couldn't open my mini fridge without cups of pudding and peanut butter and jelly sandwiches tumbling out. I collected and hoarded food compulsively, stocking away bags of Lays potato chips as if a famine were coming. If nothing else, I was going to gain weight for these babies and give them the nutrition they needed (not that there was any nutrition coming from chips or pudding, but you get my drift).

The next obsession was TV. I soon compiled a complex schedule that would take me from morning till night, binge-watching one show after the next. I didn't allow myself to turn the TV on until 10:00 a.m. (*Live with Kelly*), because if I did, the morning would drag on and I would never make it to lunch (*Barefoot

*Contessa*). Food Network then took up early afternoons, followed by copious amounts of HGTV, then on to Netflix originals by nightfall. This became my day-to-day survival routine. Each show that ended was another hour toward my babies' development. *Sons of Anarchy* and Jax Taylor quite possibly could have been the reasons I made it through bedrest.

My 6 foot 4 husband slept on the narrow hospital couch for four weeks straight. He would not leave my side, save for going to work. For that I will always love the guy. Talk about a partner in life; he was and is truly amazing. He did not get one good night's rest for an entire month, and as many times as I told him he should sleep at home, he wouldn't. His unyielding support was what got me through those agonizing weeks. He is truly the love of my life. And, to be fair, he did get a large pancake breakfast every morning.

# WE FINALLY MADE IT

Christmas was an exciting day for me. It was the first time I was allowed outside the four walls of my hospital room in three weeks. Mackey got to wheel me, albeit in my hospital bed, to the elevator and up to the third floor to do a little window shopping at the hospital store. Every girl's dream, right? The store was closed, the lights were off, and the most exciting piece of merchandise was a crocheted cardigan that I wouldn't be caught dead in. Perspective is everything, though. To break out of that room felt like a trip to the Pacific Islands.

All our family members came to visit and brought food (and more food) and gifts. Mackey and I spent the night enjoying a crab cake dinner bedside (thanks to Mom for bringing her famous crab cakes) and talking about how next year we would have the greatest Christmas of all time, complete with two little baby boys crawling under the trec.

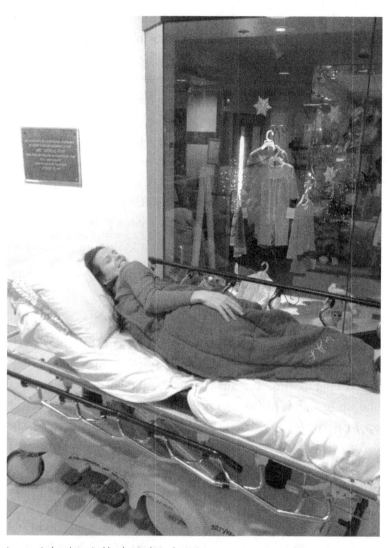

Lauren in her hospital bed, window shopping
at the hospital gift shop, Christmas 2011.

Fast-forward five days later and I was still holding out, my optimism starting to lift. I had made it to twenty-four weeks gestation. Now this was what truly felt like Christmas. The date was December 30. We hugged and cried and celebrated and probably opened a bottle of champagne. Yes, I am in the camp of "a glass of wine or champers during pregnancy is a great stress relief." Lord knows I needed some relief.

Unfortunately, this was also the same day when we got a visit from Dr. K to discuss preemie survival rates. He warned us over and over again that while we might choose to resuscitate these babies if they were to come during the next week, the likelihood that they would have any quality of life was minimal. He spouted out facts about disabilities, both cognitive and physical, as well as birth defects.

"Yes, these babies could survive, but the probability is that they will never lead a normal life. Which means you both as parents will never lead a normal life," he said. Mackey and I just looked at each other, knowing that we were both on the same page.

# A DIFFERENT PERSPECTIVE

After Dr. K left, we got a visit from the head of the Neonatal Intensive Care Unit, or NICU, Dr. H. He was a big broad teddy bear of a man with a Russian accent. Dr. H quietly sat down and told us about the risks of preemies and survival rates. The outcomes did not seem as bad as what Dr. K had just told us, or what I had read on the internet, or the endless blogs I had been reading for the last four weeks.

He explained how far modern medicine had come in keeping these super preemies alive and their improved chances of a normal life expectancy. Positive news. He was the yin to Dr. K's yang. The picture he painted was entirely different.

Even before Dr. H's visit, Mackey and I had come to the same realization: God wanted us to have these babies and it was up to us to give them a fighting chance no matter what. If they were born next week, we were absolutely 100 percent going to give them every chance to survive.

That night Mackey brought in steaks and mint chocolate chip brownie sundaes, and we had a bedside gourmet dinner as a date night. We were celebrating our twenty-four-week milestone. I went to bed soon after and at that point I was feeling A-okay. Little did I know what was to come.

I woke up at 1:30 a.m. feeling a sudden urge to pee. I called the nurse for a bedpan and she quickly came in. I began to pee—and kept peeing and peeing and peeing. Oh shit shit shit shit shit! I called out for Mackey to wake up. The nurse told me that they would have to test to see if my water had broken. We sat in silence as the doctor on call came in. She told us that she would be performing a vaginal exam where they introduce a small piece of litmus paper to determine the presence of amniotic fluid.

Two minutes later, she confirmed the worst. In a monotone, lifeless voice, she said that I would be going to labor and delivery. I wanted to literally shake this freaking doctor to death, scream at her, "How can you act so unsympathetic and indifferent when I am about to deliver twenty-four-week twins?"

We were rushed off to labor and delivery. They quickly started me on a magnesium pump, and I immediately started to feel like complete and utter dogshit. Magnesium, or mag for short, is used to help stop or slow preterm labor by relaxing the muscle tissues and slowing down contractions. While magnesium doesn't always stop the labor, it can significantly delay it in order to buy time to administer a forty-eight-hour dose of steroids that aid in baby lung development. These antenatal steroids are given to the mother and are primarily used to speed up lung development in preterm fetuses by increasing lubrication in the lungs, which helps the air sacs slide against one another without sticking together when the infant breathes.

The side effects of the magnesium are brutal for the mother. It feels like you are battling the most severe flu of your life. New mantra: "Forty-eight hours, lung development, forty-eight hours." This regimen had begun the minute they had confirmed my water had broken.

These forty-eight hours were probably the worst of my life. I was basically in and out of consciousness and every minute that passed by felt like an hour. I couldn't even speak to tell Mackey and our moms (who had rushed home from Florida that night) just how badly I felt. I later came to find out that they had miscalculated my mag dosage and given me entirely too much for my body weight. Awesome. No wonder I felt like every inch of my body was on fire. Oh well, all that mattered was that it worked and my contractions had stopped. At 1:00 a.m. on January 2, they gave me my last dose of steroids and stopped my mag drip. This was a huge win.

By 10:00 the next morning, I was feeling on top of the world, celebrating with a McDonald's breakfast that could feed a family of six. My contractions had stopped for the most part, and the head nurse came in to tell me that they were going to transfer me back to the high-risk unit. Absolutely fantastic news. Who knew I would be so excited to go back to my four-walled prison at the other wing of the hospital. But just as they were making the phone call to put in the transfer, I felt a contraction. Then another. The nurse told me I would likely be having these for the near future.

I fooled myself into thinking that if the medical team didn't think it was a big deal, then maybe it wasn't. But deep down I knew. Soon they were coming on like fast-breaking waves. I could see the contractions on the monitor growing larger and larger by the minute. The nurse was nowhere to be found.

"Mackey, go find a doctor, any doctor," I cried. I knew in my bones the babies were coming, and we needed to act fast.

A few minutes later, Mackey rushed back in with my doctor, who took one look at the monitor and quickly decided that we needed to do an emergency C-section. Mom was right by my side, reassuring me that everything would be okay.

"You are in good hands, you made it to twenty-four weeks, you can do this," she told me. Ten minutes later I was wheeled into the delivery room, about to start the fight of my life for these two little creatures that I was both terrified and excited to meet. As we entered the delivery room, I was taken aback by how many people were there. Four doctors, four nurses, and an eight-person crew of NICU staff (four nurses/docs for each baby). It all seemed so surreal. As the full weight of the situation came crashing down, panic set in.

# 11

# LACEY: FELIZ FUCKING NAVIDAD

As we made our way to the gate at Baltimore airport on Christmas Eve morning, it felt like a ghost town with hardly anyone around. The reality that Ben and I would be spending the holiday alone in Mexico started to hit me, making me feel a bit lonely. At this point I had failed eight transfers and had moved on to surrogacy, only to have my carrier unable to get pregnant on the first transfer. I was feeling a bit low and lonely and hoping that some sunshine would cure my mood, with the holiday still on my mind.

I imagined my family having our usual Christmas Eve lunch after Lauren and I finished running our five-mile loop, followed by a cozy church service with Father Jack, a family friend who had married Ben and me. Then we would head back to my parents' house for a big Christmas Eve party with around 100 people celebrating together. It's always been one of the highlights of my year, and I was missing it. But I knew that enduring another year of questions about my possible pregnancy was not an option, and we had made the right decision.

It was still tough, and I didn't realize how much I would miss our annual traditions until that moment. The beach had always been my happy place, so I hoped it would be a lovely distraction and that the next forty-eight hours would fly by. Christmas needed to come and go as quickly as possible.

After a quick three-hour flight, we arrived at the Cancun airport, went through customs, and hailed a taxi to take us to our hotel. As soon as we stepped out of the airport and into the warm sunshine, I immediately felt calmer. However, I wasn't prepared for the sight of the hotel teeming with little kids and families all there to celebrate the holiday. Despite that, I tried to focus on the fact that I was on a beautiful vacation with Ben, which was much needed.

## MONTEZUMA'S REVENGE

Before our trip, Ben and I had reserved a fancy Christmas Eve dinner at the Rosewood, a nearby hotel. We spent half a day traveling and the other half soaking up some sun on the beach before dressing up and heading over to the restaurant on a golf cart. The evening began to feel magical, and I could feel all the stress that I had been carrying around with me for the last few months start to slowly dissipate.

We were halfway through our first cocktail at the bar when Ben looked at me with concern on his face. It came on so quickly, from out of nowhere. He has a weak stomach, known as the infamous "O'Neil stomach," and I was hoping it was what we call "a gripper"—a one and done, enema style. But that wasn't the case. He suddenly became so nauseous that we had to leave before we could even sit down for dinner.

As we left our half-full drinks at the bar and golf-carted home, any glimpse of a magical Christmas Eve shattered. I was incredibly bummed about missing this dinner, as I had been stalking the restaurant's website for a couple of weeks. Lauren and I had already picked out my entrée and dessert for God's sake. The foodie in me was looking forward to this first night, and lo and behold, it was spent in our hotel room (and Ben in the bathroom). I can't say that I didn't feel sorry for myself, but my priority was getting Ben better. I prayed it would be a quick sickness, so as not to ruin our entire trip.

# ROOM SERVICE FOR ONE

We ended up spending our entire Christmas Eve in our hotel room with me eating room service for one and watching crappy TV while Ben dealt with the dreadful norovirus. This should not have surprised me as my luck was pretty crappy these days. What was one more blow to the gut?

The next day, Christmas morning, Ben was so debilitatingly sick, he was confined to bed and, of course, the bathroom. He skipped breakfast and lunch and was bedridden all day long. Sadly, I left him in a dark and gloomy hotel room and ventured out to fend for myself. Sitting at a table for one, I was left to eat Christmas breakfast on my own, watching multiple joyous families enjoy a festive holiday meal. With the day ahead of me, I headed to the beach and tried to enjoy my day, all the while hoping it would pass quickly.

Later that day on my way back to our room, I stopped to call my family from the lobby pay phone. They had been on my mind all day, as I thought about all the festivities I was missing. I caught them right in time, reaching them before they were about to sit down to Christmas dinner.

Lauren answered my parents' phone, hoping it was me. The minute I heard "hello," her familiar voice made me yearn all the more for home and our holiday traditions. Lauren wanted to hear all about Mexico and the resort, and when she asked about the Christmas Eve dinner, I told her the sad truth. She told me how lonely her morning run was without me, and I vowed to be back home again next year, running by her side. She obviously missed me, but she also knew that this trip was about self-preservation. Lauren stayed on the phone a few more minutes, not wanting to get off as she knew I was at a true low point. She was currently experiencing her own infertility hell with her most recent miscarriage; we understood each other's pain in the way that no one else could. She eventually said her goodbye and passed the phone to Mom, who also was eager to hear from me.

In the background I could hear all the laughter, noise, and banter of the rest of our extended family enjoying the evening. Mom told me the menu she had planned—tenderloin and crab cakes, her famous specialties—and how my cousins had successfully arrived from out of town. We talked about my adorable niece and nephews for a bit and what Santa brought them. I asked a million questions, trying to keep my mom on the phone, not wanting to let her go. I simply did not want the call to end, and I dreaded the idea of hanging up.

I had hardly talked to anyone all day and it was Christmas. I was desperately missing them and feeling very alone in Mexico. Finally, Mom said, "Lace, I am so sorry, but I must get going. I need to get dinner on the table for fifteen people, and I'm nowhere near ready."

I responded as I knew she needed me to do. "Of course, Mom. You go. I know you have a lot to do," I said in the bravest voice I could muster. "I'll call you guys again tomorrow. Tell everyone that I love them, and Merry Christmas again."

And then the line went dead. I pushed back tears and took a little walk to center myself before I headed back to the room to face the prospect of Christmas dinner alone. Fortunately, I have a husband who is tough and was feeling a bit better. Ben was determined not to let me eat dinner alone on Christmas night.

Right at the moment when I needed it most, he rebounded and was there for me. He willed himself to feel better and got showered and dressed so we could have a memorable Christmas dinner together.

As I like to say, mind over matter. He was going to suck it up so I wouldn't have to be alone. Hand in hand, we headed down to the hotel restaurant and ate dinner on a romantic, sea view patio next to a thirty-foot, beautifully lit, beaming Christmas tree. It was 75 degrees and the sky that night was magical, with every star shining brighter than usual. Over dinner we talked about our year ahead and vowed to have a positive attitude and to stay strong, together, as a family of two. We lived in the moment that night and promised ourselves that we would try to continue to do so moving forward.

Lacey and Ben on Christmas night, December 25, 2020.

Fortunately, Christmas night turned out to be perfect, incredibly memorable, and just what we needed. Mexico became a true turning point for us. It rejuvenated us, helping us see the beauty in the world, and to remember how much we loved each other. We alone were enough and would make it all work some way, somehow.

That trip helped us take a step back and breathe, removing the sense of urgency and dread that we so often felt. I always said that when things got bad, we would travel and realize that life was so much bigger than the bubble we might be stuck in.

It is so important to realize what brings you passion and to indulge in that passion as you are going through infertility. Find what ignites you, use it as a distraction, and build on it. Despite the rocky start, Mexico saved us. I recognize how fortunate we were to be able to travel, and that that good fortune might not be available for everyone. But it is important to find a passion, be it hiking, reading, knitting, biking, Pilates, yoga, running, cooking, and so on. Focus on it and let it bring you happiness. Honestly, it can save you. What is your Mexico?

# 12

# LACEY: ONLY RAINBOWS AFTER THE RAIN

Once we returned from Mexico, we were full charge ahead, starting another frozen embryo transfer (FET) with our surrogate Becky. I still had tremendous faith in her, but this time I kept my expectations in check, feeling incredibly stoic and hardened about the entire process. I did not let my mind wander to the what ifs but instead tried to live in the present and focus on the day at hand.

When we got to day thirteen of the two-week wait, I reiterated to myself that a positive outcome was unlikely. Yet when the day came for Becky's pregnancy test, a glimmer of hope kept creeping up inside me. That is the thing about this process. No matter how hardened or discouraged you become, hope always seems to shine through. Or maybe it's just that I am an optimistic person and believe good things come to those who wait. Regardless of what it was, here we were once again, on pins and needles, knowing the outcome was in God's hands, not ours.

That morning, I struggled to consume my favorite vanilla latte, and only managed to eat some oatmeal out of habit, unwilling to skip a meal. However, everything changed when I received a call from Dr. Mottla at around 11:45 a.m. As I picked up the phone, I held my breath in anticipation.

He wasted no time getting to the point. "Lacey," he exclaimed, "you're going to be a mother! Becky is pregnant." I could hear the smile in his voice, and my heart swelled with joy. Finally, after so much waiting and hoping, I was going to hold my own baby in my arms. He explained to me that her hCG numbers were very strong, possibly twin strong, and that he was very encouraged with how this pregnancy was starting off. With a lump in my throat, I thanked him for the call and hung up with a feeling of hope swelling inside. As I returned to my desk, I couldn't help but grin from ear to ear, my excitement almost palpable. Becky's hCG levels were high, a promising sign, but we still had to be cautious. We decided to keep the news to ourselves and only told our family, not wanting to tempt fate with premature announcements.

As much as we looked forward to the day when we could shoot our happy news from the rooftops, we hadn't figured out the perfect way to tell our friends. How do we explain to them that it's Becky who's pregnant, not me? It was a delicate situation that required careful consideration, but for now, we were beyond excited knowing that we were on our way to becoming parents.

After two more rising hCG blood tests, we were scheduled to go in for our first heartbeat sonogram at eight weeks. On Friday, February 13, 2011, Becky, Greg, Ben, and I arrived at the all-too-familiar offices of Shady Grove in Annapolis for what we hoped would be the first view of our baby's heartbeat. In my opinion, Dr. Mottla couldn't get the ultrasound wand inside Becky fast enough. Yet there it was, the most amazing sight my eyes had ever seen. A flicker so strong and bright, there was no denying it was my baby making his or her presence known to us. It was such a strong and vibrant heartbeat; I knew in my gut that this little warrior was to be my "miracle baby."

To say it was surreal would not do it justice. The sound of the thump, thump, thump was the most beautiful music we had ever heard. Our baby's beating heart signaling all of the love, life, and happiness in our world; I wanted to stay in that room with the monitor hooked up to Becky for the next ten months (and wait on her hand and foot while doing so). There is no other tangible way to explain it. I unconditionally loved that heartbeat already, and I did not want to leave my baby then, now, or ever. Little did I know, however, the roller coaster ride was not entirely over.

Over the weekend, I received a call from Becky that sent chills down my spine. She calmly tried to break the news to me that she was bleeding. My legs felt weak, and I could barely stand, much less utter words of encouragement to her. We immediately called Dr. Mottla and arranged to go in for another sonogram first thing Monday morning. He reassured us, though, that this can happen in the early stages of pregnancy and told us to try to remain positive until Monday's appointment.

As we entered the office on Monday morning, I thought I may have a heart attack at any moment as my heart beat out of control. We waited a very long ten minutes in the waiting room, with our minds wandering in every which way. Becky sat, fidgeting with her hands, while I sat in silence and prayed like I had never prayed before. I tried to reassure myself that a little blood loss during pregnancy was normal, but I couldn't shake off the fear that something was wrong.

Luckily, I was the one who was wrong this time. Everything was still on track and looking great. The sonogram revealed that Becky had a subchorionic hematoma, a pocket of blood in her uterus that could resolve itself within a few days. Despite the diagnosis, the relief I felt was immense. As the hematoma disappeared, we saw that precious heartbeat again, and the sigh of relief we breathed was monumental. In that moment, we knew that we were willing to face any challenges and do whatever it took to bring our baby into the world. Our love for each other and our unborn child only grew stronger, and we were ready to face whatever lay ahead.

Over the next few months, I attended every doctor's appointment with Becky, even the tiny, quick weigh-ins. I was in love with my baby inside her and couldn't get enough time with her, no matter how hard I tried. I loved being in Becky's presence, knowing that she was still pregnant and knowing I was near my baby. The sight of her belly was a tangible sign that everyone was healthy.

Our twenty-week ultrasound appointment was a milestone. The four of us (me, Ben, Greg, and Becky) and Becky's youngest daughter who was three at the time, crammed into the ultrasound room, marveling over the baby's ten tiny toes and fingers. We did not find out the sex of the baby because we wanted to be surprised (and I secretly didn't want to let my mind get too attached to this baby until he or she was born). But Becky said that she was craving lemons, exactly as she had when she was pregnant with her first baby girl. When Becky mentioned this, I headed right to the kitchen and made her endless lemon bars. I also sent her lemon chicken noodle soup and lemon pound cake. And homemade lemonade. And anything else lemon that I could think to whip up (P.S.: I am not a cook but damn if I didn't try to cook for Becky). Unconsciously I was nesting, trying to care for my baby and the "oven" that was baking her.

It was around the twenty-week mark when we decided to tell people our exciting news. It was a bit awkward as there was no playbook for how to approach this. I'm not good when it comes to feelings. Do I just blurt it out over lunch with friends? I was also worried about how this alternative way to bring our baby into the world might be viewed. I mean we weren't exactly doing things the conventional way here. Luckily, we had surrounded ourselves with supportive and amazing people, and everyone was incredibly happy for us. They knew the pain we had endured and were ecstatic that we were finally going to have a baby—no matter what path we took to get there.

Surrogacy was not as widespread as it is now, and I had to explain to people in great detail how it all works. It was important to me that everyone knew that the baby was ours biologically. It was as if I needed to stake claim to my child. That seems silly to me now, but it gave me comfort at the time. I would go on to learn from my lawyer that Becky had no rights over my baby, since the baby was not biologically related to her at all. All parental rights were established to Ben and me through what's called a pre-birth order, stating that Becky will hand over the baby once he or she is born.

Leading up to the birth we were blessed with two beautiful baby showers, which helped make the reality of our soon-to-be parenthood sink in. As we sat in our baby's room, surrounded by all the gear and gifts we had received, it was a surreal moment. We couldn't believe that we were finally going to be parents. As we gazed at the tiny clothes, toys, and decorations, we knew that our lives were about to change forever. The thought of holding our precious baby in our arms filled us with a sense of joy and wonder that words could not describe. We were ready for this new chapter in our lives and excited to see what the future held.

---

Fast-forward nine months: September 9, 2011. I had finally allowed myself to believe the unbelievable: that I would soon be a mom. Always one to find an occasion to take a trip, we decided on one final trip as a family of two. A babymoon as some people say. Thankfully, Ben's frequent work-related travels had earned us a significant number of points that we could use for vacations. It was the perfect opportunity to take a break and enjoy some quality time together before the baby's arrival. So, we decided to embark on a trip out west to Deer Valley, Utah.

We were excited to have one final trip as a couple, to relax and enjoy each other's company before our little one arrived in early October. Leading up to the trip, Ben was working in Dallas, and our plan was to meet up in Utah for a weekend filled with hiking, mountain biking, indulging in good food and drinks, and, most importantly, enjoying each other's company.

If it all worked out, these would be some of the last quiet times with just the two of us. It didn't seem real, but soon enough our home would be filled with the sounds of a baby. We were very excited for the journey ahead, and we were determined to make the most of these final times together.

Windows down, cruising along I-97 on my way to the airport, I reflected on this trip and where I was in life: I was going on a babymoon because I was going to be a mom. Was this real? An instantaneous feeling of doubt set in and my anxieties took hold of me. The devil came creeping into my consciousness: Was something bad going to happen? Was I setting myself up for yet another disappointing outcome? Could this miracle really happen for me?

As if God himself was my personal DJ, a song came on the radio and as I listened to it, it was miraculously as if a veil was lifting from me, transforming my world. I will forever feel like it was a personal message for me.

This Andy Grammer song, "Keep Your Head Up," brand new at the time, spoke directly to me. Peace and calm filled my soul. "Only rainbows after rain, the sun will always come again." My rainbow was around the corner. My sunshine was on its way, and things would turn out just fine. This new sense of serenity and hope for the future that I was feeling was the best way to jump start our babymoon. If we could keep our heads up, we were going to be okay.

In this moment I finally knew what got us through all our lowest moments. And I realized something else too. Looking back on this journey, I realized this is what we had always done—kept our heads up no matter how dark the days were. And boy were there some dark days.

# THE DAY FINALLY COMES

On the eve of our miracle baby's birth, we gathered with our families for a special celebratory dinner at my parents' house. It was an evening filled with love and excitement as we eagerly anticipated the arrival of our little one. Ben and I, along with his parents, Bob and Karen, spent the night at my parents' house in Baltimore, which was just a mile away from the hospital where our baby was being delivered. Lauren and Mackey came over for a drink to toast the impending birth and share in our excitement of the next day. Always my other half, Lauren was almost as excited as I was for the birth.

As we sat around the dinner table, savoring homemade jumbo lump crab cakes and a couple of bottles of Santa Margarita, we couldn't help but talk about our baby and wonder what sex and size he or she would be. I had a strong feeling that our baby would be a boy, possibly because of my own family dynamics where the oldest child was a boy, and because of my experience with losing twin boys. Yet keeping the sex a surprise made it even more special and exciting of a day.

Even though we were all excited, I couldn't shake off the feeling of disbelief that this was all really happening. It felt like a dream that I wouldn't wake up from until I held our baby in my arms. But for that evening, we celebrated the miracle of life and the love of family. We truly enjoyed our last night childless.

The next morning, after a long run with Lauren in hopes of releasing some of my jitters, the time had come to meet our baby. At 10:00 a.m., with our car seat perfectly installed in the back seat, we arrived at the hospital bursting with anxious excitement. After check-in, we were escorted back to the pre-op room where Becky and Greg waited before entering the operating room. Looking at Becky and her tiny belly, I wondered how in the world she had my baby in there. The most amazing thing about Becky and her pregnancies was that she usually only gained the weight of the baby over those ten months. (Not fair, right? This woman was destined to be a surrogate.) Throughout her entire pregnancy, she had only gained 7 pounds, and I was slightly terrified of how small my baby would be.

The operating room was packed with so many people who wanted to witness this incredibly happy moment. Our OB, the anesthesiologist, numerous nurses, Becky, Greg, Ben, and I all piled in. After they rolled her in, I walked over and took my place by Becky's head, wanting to be there to support her and make sure she was okay. Greg held her hand on the other side of the bed, and Ben waited anxiously by the drape hoping to catch the first glimpse of our baby.

As they began the C-section, it felt as if time was standing still. The entire surgery and birth were a maximum of five minutes but felt like years. All I wanted to see and hear was a screaming, healthy baby. Biting my lip to hold back four years of built-up tears, I waited as they tugged and pulled to get our little son out. Eventually they grabbed hold of the little bum and wiggled the baby out. Our ob proudly held the baby up exclaiming, "She looks great! Congratulations, you have a perfectly healthy baby girl." She? It was a GIRL? A baby *girl*! Our baby girl. Oh, and did she scream! It was the most beautiful sound I ever heard. I rushed to her, as they cleaned her off, and stared at her with amazement. Unrelenting tears of pure joy streamed down my face as I held our baby for the first time. It was the most perfect moment of my life.

My body shook with love, gratitude, and humility. She was the most splendid creature in the entire world. Ben beamed from ear to ear, completely smitten with this little angel. We cut her umbilical cord and wrapped her up, my shoulders shuddering from uncontrollable sobs. I bawled tears of happiness as I introduced Becky to the baby that she had been carrying for the last ten months, our daughter. The words *thank you* are never enough in this situation. She, who less than a year ago had been a stranger, gave me the most profound gift a human can give. A baby girl. There is not a day that goes by that I do not say a prayer of thanks for Becky. Until my dying breath, I will live in humble gratitude for her.

After Becky was sewed up, she was taken back to her recovery room. How strange it must feel for her right now, I thought. How in the world do you thank someone for doing this? I mean, I realized that we had mutually entered a contract, and she was well compensated, but this gift transcended money. There was no sum that could express how we felt.

Ben and I took our baby back to the nursery where I fed her for the first time. We quietly sat, gazing at her, in awe and wonder. She was just so beautiful and healthy, staring up at me with her huge brown eyes, just like mine. All the pain of the last four years vanished immediately. I happily fed her as Ben sprinted to the waiting room to tell our families the great news.

While I was feeding her, the nurse asked what her name was.

"Hmm," I responded. "She doesn't have a name because I was sure she'd be a boy. I had my boy's name picked. Our possible girl's name was Phoebe, but she doesn't look like a Phoebe to me. So, I don't know!"

"Well, what was your boy's name?" the nurse asked.

"Miller," I replied, "after my maiden name, Aumiller."

"Then name her Miller," the nurse went on. "You could call her Milly. In Spanish, my language, *Mili* is short for *milagra* and means little miracle. It seems incredibly fitting, right?"

After looking up additional meanings of the name, I found variations—gentle strength, strong in work, brave strength. Well, that settled it. This name was perfect. Ben and I agreed that Miller would go by Milly, as she was our very own little miracle.

Of course, I needed to run the name by Lauren, who was currently pregnant herself. I always valued her opinion. And Ben concurred with his sister to make sure she liked it too. But we had agreed, Milly she would be.

Bringing Lauren back into the nursery for the first time was magical. We had both endured so much and there was finally a baby in our lives, and two more on the way as she was newly pregnant with twins. We were both so emotional and cried tears of joy, agreeing that this little Milly was perfect.

That night in the hospital, Ben, Milly, and I were given a small room that was often used for adoptive parents. It was about 10x10 and held only a twin bed and a small side table with a single desk lamp. While most babies slept in the nursery, Ben and I refused to let Milly out of our sight. She slept in the room with us, in her bassinet, as we marveled at her every coo.

Lacey and Ben hold newborn Milly as they arrive home from the hospital, October 11, 2011

Sharing a single bed that night in the hospital, I told Ben that I felt transformed by Milly's birth and my body felt oddly different. Did I want to have sex with Ben right then? My hormones were raging, I could feel it. Was sex actually on my mind right now? I laughed and said to him, "For some reason, I want to jump your bones!"

This was not the feeling I thought I would have on the first night with our newborn daughter in the room, but my body felt so alive. What was going on inside of me? It was as if there was a shift in my entire being, all the way to my core. And as I would soon discover, it was a real one.

# 13

# LAUREN: THE UNIMAGINABLE

After four weeks on bedrest with a cervical stitch that was barely holding strong, my body had had enough. I was 100 percent going into labor and there was no stopping these babies from coming. The next thing I knew, I was quickly being sliced open. The only thing I heard in the large sterile delivery room were the hushed directions of the doctors. Not a word was uttered from the nurses or others in the room for fear of interrupting their work. Mackey was standing by my head holding my hand. He would occasionally whisper to me what the doctors were doing, "Okay, they are making the incision," but for the most part, he was transfixed by the gory procedure that was unfolding.

After what seemed like only a few short minutes, the doctors lifted each of my tiny babies from my belly. They were now out of the safety of my womb, and all I felt was fear. Fear of the unknown. The entire NICU crew went to work immediately, assessing the babies and getting them on oxygen.

Brady and Jud were born at 1:03 p.m. and 1:05 p.m., respectively, weighing 1 pound 10 ounces and 1 pound 12 ounces. By definition, babies born before twenty-eight weeks are considered extremely premature and require many weeks of intensive care. They were twenty-four weeks and three days gestation. But all I could think of was that my babies had made it into this world alive. I was so thankful.

Although Brady and Jud were fraternal twins (two egg sacs), they looked identical. Both blueish in skin color, with eyes sealed shut (babies generally begin to open their eyes around twenty-six weeks). Every one of their little bones showed through their thin skin. They did not look anything like the little chubby newborns I had envisioned in my head. I had never seen a super preemie before, and to be honest, I was shocked at first. They were so very small. They looked like tiny little animals, almost skeletal. Yet I loved everything about these itty-bitty, bird-like creatures.

Immediately, they were both intubated and whisked from me to the neonatal intensive care unit.

After the boys were taken away, I was wheeled to the postpartum unit and immediately fell into one of the deepest sleeps of my life. After forty-eight hours on a magnesium drip, followed by the emotional turmoil of delivering twenty-four-week twins, coupled with all the drugs given for the delivery, I was beyond exhausted. I was in an alternate state, completely out of myself.

Five hours later, I awoke from the deepest sleep of my life. Utter panic hit me hard. "Mackey, Mackey," I screamed as I came to, "how are the boys, where are they?"

"They are doing fine at the moment. Remember, they are in the NICU, babe," he assured me.

"I need to go there now, please take me there right now."

The next two days were extremely scary, but for the most part, both boys were doing okay. We were told they were in the "honeymoon period," which is the few days post-birth where micro-preemies remain relatively stable, having only recently been in the mom's womb.

"It seems like they are defying the odds," I kept telling Mack. "Our little wimpy white boys aren't so wimpy at all." The term "wimpy white boys" was a NICU description. Statistically, Caucasian male preemies had the worst survival rates once outside the womb.

I went back and forth from my hospital room on the first floor to the NICU on the fourth floor. I still required monitoring after my C-section and there were no beds in the NICU rooms. So Mackey and I traveled back and forth from post-partum to NICU, holding our breath each time we arrived at their hospital rooms.

Usually moms are able to do "skin-to-skin," or "Kangaroo Care" with their newborn babies. This involves the mother laying the baby, clothed in only a diaper, on the mother's bare chest. The baby can feel the mother's heartbeat and it quickly calms and soothes. Preemies especially benefit from this type of holding as it significantly improves blood flow to the brain and cardiac function.

Unfortunately, extremely premature babies like Brady and Jud are not allowed to do Kangaroo Care because moving them from their incubators to mom's chest is considered too stressful. Even changing their diapers can spike their blood pressure, signaling that they are in pain. All that we could do was put our hands through the holes in their incubators and cup their tiny heads and bottoms. While it was frustrating, we were grateful for whatever physical contact we could have with our baby boys.

Luckily, the babies did not have any major brain bleeds or heart issues. They were both on respirators, but they only required the expected amount of oxygen normally given to twenty-four-week preemies. We were told that the steroids for their lungs that I had been given three days earlier had most likely helped.

It seemed like every minute of every hour there were a myriad of tests being done on the boys: blood sugar levels, oxygen levels, heart and kidney scans, blood pressure stats, EKGs, MRIs. The list seemed endless. The amount of new information that we had to learn and digest felt completely overwhelming at times, yet the medical jargon quickly became our new language. Every test result was something for us to pour over and figure out, ask questions, and prepare for what lay ahead. We were constantly told that things could change in the blink of an eye.

I will always remember Dr. H telling us, "These babies can make a turn pretty quickly, so be prepared."

---

On the morning of January 4, I woke up in a panic. Little did I know that this would be how I would wake up for the next year of my life.

"Mack, Mack, MACK. No NICU calls, right, right?" I screamed. Mackey had stayed at the NICU until 1:00 a.m. the night before and I had called at 3:00 a.m. and everything was status quo. That didn't mean that I wasn't still worried though.

"No, no phone calls."

I sighed out a long heavy breath.

I quickly rang my nurse, asking her to come and take my vitals so that I could get back up to the boys.

"I'll be right there," Amy, my bubbly young nurse, said, "and don't forget, you can shower today."

Oh man, this was my lucky day. Mackey gently helped me walk into the bathroom and turned the shower on. I stepped into the scalding hot water, letting it stream down my neck and back. The stress from the past few days seemed to slough off me, circling the drain below. It had been five weeks since my last shower. That's right, five. This felt magical and luxurious. For the past five weeks I had been living in a constant state of fear about delivering still-born babies, and I felt that stress subside just a bit. An invisible weight lifted from my body. Thank you, God. Thank you.

Three minutes later, I heard the phone in my hospital room begin to ring. *Probably just Mom checking in to see how the boys are doing,* I told myself. I heard Mackey answer the phone. My breath stopped and the world became silent. Deep down, I knew who was calling; it was the NICU upstairs.

Mackey slammed down the phone. "Laur, you need to get out of the shower immediately," he said, trying to remain calm. "Jud is not doing well." The weight that only minutes before had evaporated slammed into my body with the force of a train. I couldn't see, I couldn't hear.

We rushed up to the fourth floor, Mackey quickly pushing me in the wheelchair. Looking back, all I can remember about that moment was a profound sense of fear. A fear that I had never experienced in my life before this moment. Fear of losing something that I loved more than anything I ever thought possible. Fear of being destroyed if I did lose that love. Fear of the unknown.

Dan, the respiratory therapist, was manually bagging oxygen into Jud's miniature lungs as we rushed into the room. His tiny body was shaking up and down with the force of it and his thin rail arms lay limp at his side. It was as if I was thrown into another world—a nightmarish fog. I had never experienced agony like this before.

I hadn't even kissed his sweet skin yet, and now I was seeing him slip away from me. I hadn't even held this beautiful baby. I could tell he was in pain and trying to hold on, and all I wanted to do was hold him in my arms and nuzzle his tiny little cheeks. But I could do nothing more than talk to him and pray. "Be strong, Jud. Please be strong. But it's also okay if you have to go. It's okay, sweetie. We love you and we understand."

After thirty minutes of resuscitation attempts, the doctor called Jud's death. His lungs were simply not strong enough to support him. The bagging stopped and with it came tears from the entire room. I was unable to breathe because of the watermelon-sized lump of sheer devastation in my throat. I choked on my tears as Mackey pulled me in and I rested my head on his heaving chest. Streams of tears fell from everyone's eyes. We all hugged each other, prayed, and sobbed. Life had become completely and utterly changed forever. How would I move on from this? Could I?

Judy, a nurse that we had come to love and trust over the past two days, picked Jud up ever so gently and handed me my beautiful baby boy. My body ached in a way I'd never experienced. It was not fair that this was the first time that I got to hold him. He never got to feel the sensation of lying on my chest, my heart pouring out the love to him that could fill an entire ocean. He was still warm as I laid him on my chest and imagined his pure little soul floating up to heaven. My God, why? The only thing I knew was that Brady now had his own guardian angel. My Jud would be there to get his brother through the trying times that lay ahead. This much I knew.

We held Jud in our arms for the rest of the afternoon and said our goodbyes to our baby boy. We told him how proud we were of him and how much love we had for him and would always have. We told him all about heaven, or at least what we knew about it, and how happy he would be there. We asked him to watch over his brother.

-------

Later that night, Mackey and I went into Brady's hospital room. We were told earlier that he was having a stable day. From the moment we walked through the door, we sensed Jud's protective presence. His tiny little body was still in the room next door, but his soul and spirit were now with Brady. Brady turned a bit of a corner in those hours. He ended up having a "great night," something that rarely occurs in the NICU so early on. You come to hold onto these little triumphs with irrational strength.

Jud had given all of his strength and spirit to Brady that night. It was the closest I've come to having a true religious and spiritual experience. There was a tangible, protective, healing energy that radiated from Brady's little body. It was as though Jud had given his life for his brother's.

Around 2:00 a.m., when we finally lay down in bed that night, a feeling of guilt washed over me—a guilt that would stay with me until this very day. Why had my body not been strong enough to carry Jud longer, to let his lungs develop fully? I brought him into this world too early, and I was responsible for my son not getting to live a full life. This guilt would then transfer over to Brady and his struggle in the NICU. With every prick of his foot for a blood test, or breathing tube inserted down his throat, or critical surgery that left him lethargic for days, the guilt suffocated me. This was all on me. What an awful struggle I had bequeathed to these innocent children of mine.

This loss—especially after the challenges we had endured for the past three years, after wanting these babies more than anything else in my entire life—was utterly debilitating. It was a devastation that would never truly leave me, taking a piece of me that I will never get back.

I have since talked to many other mothers who have lost a child, and while each one deals with their pain differently, we all have one thing in common: We are changed forever.

You are not meant to lose your child. That being said, I realized that I did not lose a five-year-old child, or a twenty-five-year-old child. I do believe that is different. I didn't have years upon years of memories of Jud or know his personality. I do not have those memories that other parents who have lost older children have, which I am sure would bring me to my knees with pain. I don't have photos of birthday parties or videos of him having a dance party with his siblings. To me, having those memories would make it so much harder to bear. Maybe I have it easier because I lost Jud after only two days. But one thing is certain: losing a child is the worst thing a human can experience. My worst nightmare had come true.

# 14

# LAUREN: OUR LITTLE MIRACLE

When Jud died after living only two days, I wondered how I could endure the all-consuming grief I was feeling for the loss of one son, while simultaneously supporting his twin brother, Brady. How could I navigate this torturous and convoluted road that lay ahead for my tiny baby boy?

"Mackey, I just don't know how I can get through this. I feel so broken," I whispered to my husband while lying in bed one night. "Just like you always do, Laur, just keep moving forward. And pray." So that is what I did.

Brady wound up staying in the NICU for six months, which eviscerated my spirit with each passing day. There was a stagnant, unwavering, gnawing pit in my stomach for 181 straight days. It made me physically sick, and it didn't give me even a second's reprieve. Six months of breathlessly waiting and wondering day after day if my child would live through another night. This was pure purgatory.

I will never forget Lacey picking me up to take me to Bertucci's Pizza for lunch one day. We headed there as we knew we were less likely to run into anyone. It was early on in Brady's first two weeks of life. She wanted to get me out of the hospital, and rightly so, as I had barely left those NICU walls. I remember crying uncontrollably throughout lunch, while furiously eating an entire large meat-lovers pizza on my own (I was pumping breast milk six times a day at that point and constantly ravenous).

Even though I wept throughout lunch, damn did it feel good to be a part of the outside world again. It only lasted an hour, but I could have sat in that Bertucci's booth for days, basking in the normalcy of it all.

When Lacey pulled up to the hospital to drop me off, I melted into a puddle of tears. I didn't want to go back inside. The small glimpse of the outside world was too hard. I looked at Lacey, sobbing, "This sounds awful, but I do not want to go back in there. I want to be with Brady, but every minute is pure torture in that room. All I do is sit and wait for the next shoe to drop."

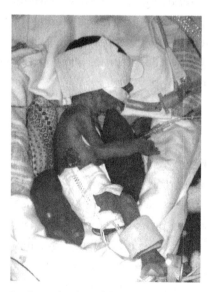

Brady, twelve days old in the NICU,
January 14, 2012.

I did not want to return to the agonizing torment that had become my life. Will my Brady Boy die or survive? Will I *still* be childless after all of this? Lacey, as always, had the perfect words of encouragement for me.

"Laur, you have only been a mom for a few short weeks, but I can tell you right now, you are the strongest mama I have ever seen."

I finally collected myself and made my way back to the NICU.

# FEEDING BRADY

My typical day while Brady was in the NICU started with me waking up around 6:00 a.m. and doing my first breast milk pump of the day. I lived and died by the breast pump—two large suction cups constantly attached to my sore-as-hell nipples. Even though Brady was not yet ready for breast milk, I was told that it was extremely beneficial for preemies, so damned if I wasn't going to pump my ass off—or what felt like my nipples off. I was told that as he got a bit stronger, they would switch him to this "liquid gold." His stomach was still too undeveloped for milk of any kind in those first few weeks.

He was given fluids and nutrients through his PICC line. A PICC line is a long, soft, plastic tube inserted into a large vein in the baby's arm or leg where it can deliver medications or total parenteral nutrition (TPN). The procedure for inserting a PICC line takes about one to two hours to complete, and that was the first nail-biting surgery that Brady had. It was not guaranteed that he would make it through. It seemed like a miracle that he did at the time.

Brady had constant critical stomach or gut issues. If a baby doesn't have a healthy gut, he cannot receive nourishment and cannot grow stronger. We needed his stomach and intestines to develop for him to survive. The constant threat of NEC

121

(necrotizing enterocolitis), a very serious intestinal disease that can quickly take a preemie's life in a matter of hours, was always looming in our minds.

After weeks of being fed only TPN, the doctors said that we could try giving him breast milk through his tube and see how his gut was able to handle it. Up until this point I had been freezing my milk. I had already filled up our two freezers at home and was now storing it at my parents' and in-laws' houses.

Although I couldn't for the life of me get pregnant—didn't have a hormone in my body to speak of—I produced enough milk to feed a small nation. I will never forget when my father-in-law, Jud (whom our Jud was named after), called to ask if I could come and remove my milk bottles a year later so that he could get to his frozen deer meat. Ah, can't make this shit up!

When we first gave Brady breast milk, he was able to digest it for two days straight. He then stopped having bowel movements, so we quickly went back to the TPN. I was on constant watch for the signs of NEC—swollen belly, diarrhea, constipation—as I had read way too much on the internet about how fast a preemie could perish from it. We were constantly starting and stopping breast milk feeds as a way of monitoring his gut.

Brady would go days without being fed because his sensitive belly was sometimes not able to process the milk that I was now so diligently pumping for him. Every day that went by when he could not handle his feedings meant one more day that he was getting weaker. He would eventually go on to have life-saving intestinal surgery two months later.

## TOUCHING MOMENTS

During the first two months in the NICU, I would stand for hours on end, placing my hands on Brady's tiny body through the openings in his isolette. Research has shown that both maternal and paternal touch for micro-preemies is extremely comforting. In order to soothe him, we would cradle-hold him with one hand on the top of his head and the other on his bottom.

When the nurses would do a heel prick to measure his blood sugar levels, I would hold his little hand and watch his face scrunch up in pain. Extreme preemies like Brady are so weak that they really do not cry. They barely make any sound, but you can tell when they are in pain by their heart rate as well as their facial expressions. Those heel pricks, done every four hours on his tiny little feet were the worst. Especially if the nurse did not get a good stick and had to do it again.

Let's just say mama was not a happy camper when that happened. Seeing him in pain like that only sent me even further into the self-loathing guilt fest that had become my life. I stood there all day every day, my hands through the isolette, hoping that my touch would soothe him. It wasn't enough though. I wanted to hold him.

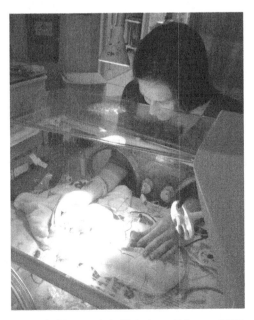

Lauren holding Brady in his isolette, February 2012.

The highlight of my days was changing Brady's tiny diaper every four hours. It was during these times that I was able to care for him as a mother should. I would gently talk and sing to him while giving him a quick wash and putting a clean diaper on. When Mackey was there, we would literally fight over who got to do the diaper change; it allowed us more contact with our love bug.

Changing a preemie's diaper is actually very stressful for the baby. They are so weak that even this simple task can quickly spike their heart rates, signaling they are in pain. The nurses told us to be as gentle as possible while also being quick so as not to disrupt him too much. We would then swaddle him and let him rest until the next change or test.

## BREATHING CHALLENGES

Because Brady's lungs weren't fully developed, he couldn't breathe on his own and had to receive oxygen through a mechanical ventilator. If Brady needed low levels of supplemental oxygen—anything below 50 percent—he was doing well, and we could relax. And 100 percent oxygen is the maximum anyone can receive. If that is not enough, there is nothing else that modern medicine can do to save the patient—in this case, my baby.

When his oxygen needs started to spike, it was doomsday. I would sit in my son's hospital room and watch one number constantly flashing on the screen: oxygen levels, or saturation levels as they call it in the NICU. Those monitors and their incessant beeping continue to haunt me to this day. Some days he would start out with 70 percent oxygen, then climb to 80 percent, then 90 percent. Life stood still and I would just stare, and pray, and the pit in my stomach would grow so large that I was sure it might consume me.

# SEPARATION ANXIETY

The doctors encouraged parents to go home in the evenings; there were no beds in the rooms, and they realized that staying at the hospital for twenty-four hours straight was unhealthy. After the first week, we started to go home at night to sleep. I was always dragging my feet leaving the NICU at the end of the day. We absolutely hated to leave Brady, but we had faith in the nurses and doctors that they would contact us if his condition changed.

So each day I would get up early to pump, and while pumping would call the NICU for an update on how the night before went. If I didn't get a middle-of-the-night call, it meant that Brady had a good night. However, most mornings I would wake up in a complete panic, reaching for my phone, afraid that I had slept through and missed one of these calls.

Those middle-of-the-night calls literally make me short of breath just thinking about them now. The call would usually go something like this: "Lauren, it's nurse Katie. Brady's oxygen levels are starting to creep up, and we didn't get good blood sugar from him. You don't have to come in, but you may want to in case anything happens."

Obviously we shot right out of bed and to the NICU upon receiving these calls. The memory of how quickly we had lost Jud was still so fresh. We knew things could take a turn for the worst in an instant.

If Brady had a decent night, the nurses would encourage me to try to get some rest and to take my time coming in the next morning. Typically, I arrived at the hospital by 8:00 a.m. to start my day of watching helplessly and learning as much about neonatal medicine as possible. I waited, watched, prayed, and asked questions.

Preemies have a myriad of tests done each day—heel sticks, oxygen levels, gut function, liver enzymes, ultrasounds, and fluid levels. They are constantly monitored and hooked up to alarms, which generally go off about once every three seconds. These alarms are enough to make you want to rip your hair out, especially considering that half the time they ended up being falsely initiated. If Brady moved a certain way or knocked off a pulse ox sensor, the whole room sounded like we were under nuclear attack.

## CONSTANT CONCERNS

Brady was in an absolute critical condition for four straight months, and each day was a new challenge. With every step forward, it seemed we took two back. Coupled with his lung and intestinal issues were an array of other life-threatening conditions to monitor involving his liver, heart, and brain. By the end of the first two weeks, I had learned more preemie terminology than any parent should have to. I was able to talk the talk, or so I thought, and was constantly questioning the doctors on protocol.

"Dr. K, do we absolutely need another ultrasound? And can't you spread the blood sugar heel sticks out just a bit more. Why are we fooling with him so much?"

Every time you so much as even touch these super preemies, you are stressing their system. After so much time spent in the NICU, I just might have considered myself somewhere in between a nurse and a nurse practitioner, minus the years of endless education and training. I was my little man's bodyguard; God help the person who was going to lay a finger on him unless absolutely necessary.

We also worried about Brady's vision; he had retinopathy—a common condition in preemies that often causes blindness. We were told that he would have to have surgery to correct this. There was a chance that the surgery would not work, and he would be blind for the rest of his life. At this point, all I wanted was for Brady to live—blind or not did not matter, I just wanted my baby here on earth with me.

There were also other non-life-threatening issues that we worried about that could arise in the future from extreme prematurity: cerebral palsy, cognitive development, and hearing loss. Each day brought more tests and more surgeries. Brady had major intestinal surgery, retinopathy surgery, hernia surgery, two different feeding tubes put in, and dozens of other procedures that left us in a constant state of fear.

It felt as if every day we were either preparing for a surgery or recovering from one. If he did have a good day, we would usually leave the NICU around 7:30 or 8:00 p.m., only to travel home to anxiously sit by the phone.

# WHATEVER IT TAKES TO GET THROUGH

My coping mechanisms became family, red wine, and any food that had more than 50 grams of sugar. My parents, or in-laws, or siblings, or all of the above would come over and we would basically drink our sorrows away. No, I don't necessarily recommend it, but you gotta do what you gotta do.

We would talk about what a rock star Brady was that day, and I would let my mind go to planning our future with him. I would also eat copious amounts of ice cream, the small batch decadent kind that really makes you feel good, and various other desserts from the meal train that our friends had so generously set up for us. Around 9:00 p.m., Mackey and I would usually try to watch an "episode" as we called it, and let Netflix ease our minds away from what was actually going on in our life.

I could not get away though. I would sit in the corner spot of our L-shaped couch and stare at my phone, waiting for the NICU to call. I knew they would phone if Brady were to have any kind of change. Nonetheless, every two hours, I would call in to check on his latest test results: oxygen levels, blood sugar levels, feeding status, heart rate, and so on.

There is one such night that I will never forget. Brady was stable at the time but had had a less than stellar day. His oxygen levels were higher than normal and had slowly crept higher over the course of a few hours that afternoon. I was a mess, my mind reeling in a state of torment. We were told to go home as he had stabilized, and if anything changed, they would call us right away.

I will never forget looking over and seeing Mackey snoring on the couch at 8:30 p.m. *How the hell is he able to sleep?* I was in the middle of a legitimate nightmare, and he was able to actually sleep. This is the difference between men and women. Mackey is an unbelievably caring and emotional man—almost to the point of what most women experience, God bless him. He is my rock and has the biggest heart of anyone I know, especially when it comes to me and our family.

Yet he was still not enduring the stress and pain and worry that I was as a mother. My maternal instinct would not allow my thoughts to wander from my baby who was suffering. It consumed every millisecond of my life.

To stay mentally strong during this time, I felt the need to cut myself off from the rest of the world. It was a defense mechanism of sorts. I spoke only to my family and two friends. I never went out for fear of running into someone at the grocery store and possibly breaking down sobbing to someone who would innocently ask how I was doing.

Besides going out to Bertucci's lunches with Lacey and hitting up Dunkin' Donuts in the mornings for coffee, the NICU was really the only place I went. I couldn't face the outside world. The well-meaning sympathetic looks that people gave me sent me over the edge. Baltimore is a small town, and everyone knew what we were going through.

As luck would have it, the only other time I did venture out was to grab breakfast when Brady was probably only a month old. Mackey and I went to a small marketplace, and as we were getting out of the car, we ran directly into the worst possible people to see at that point in time: a couple and their baby who had delivered at the same medical center two days before us. They had been in the postpartum unit with us and were acquaintances of ours from Baltimore.

I took one look at that sweet baby that they were carrying in their bucket seat, so happy and healthy, and lost it. All I could think of was poor Brady in his isolette, being pricked and prodded every other minute.

My world came crashing down. I started sobbing uncontrollably, and actually had to walk away and put myself in the car without even saying goodbye. Mackey was left standing there to apologize for me. I am usually a pretty emotionally controlled kind of gal who doesn't rush into hysterics and then awkwardly peace out on a social interaction. That one encounter was enough for me. From then on, it was the NICU and home. I could go nowhere else. I was not going to chance a run-in like that again.

I literally saw no one. It was a bit like when I was going through all of those in vitros again. I turned down every social invitation, hoping only to stay close to those I felt safe with and who knew what I was going through. It was just easier that way. But unlike in vitro, where I was subconsciously feeling a sense of shame for not being able to get pregnant, this isolation was a means of protecting myself from a different type of pain. Not having to have to explain, or cry, or hear people's condolences seemed like the best way for me to bear this trying time.

I often talk to other parents who are going through an experience similar to mine, whether it be infertility or time in the NICU, and my advice is always the same: If you are feeling like you have cut yourself off from people, or have become somewhat of a social recluse, cut yourself some slack. It is called self-preservation, and we all deal with our issues in different ways. Just remember that you do need a few close people to lean on because you can't go it alone. We need people to hold us up and strengthen us along the way.

# MY PEEPS

I have always had Lacey as well as a small crew of amazing friends to get me through the trying times—bad breakups, issues at school or sports, problems at work. When it came to people I truly leaned on during this time, it was Lacey and my mom, Sue.

To put it simply, Lacey feels my pain and joy, and vice versa. She will always be the older sister in our relationship, and she takes on my pain just as I do hers. I can't stand to see her unhappy; it breaks my heart. I know how lucky I am, and I thank God daily for having her in my life. I can always count on her to give me advice, tell me that things are going to work out, or pick me up when I am at my absolute lowest. She is a part of me to my core, my other half. We unknowingly mirror each other in thoughts, feelings, and actions. To have someone to tell your darkest secrets, fears, wants, and thoughts to is priceless.

Mom is the epitome of what a mom should be and what I aspire to be. During this time, she, too, was in a constant state of pain for the sake of Brady, but even more from seeing her daughter endure such suffering. There is a reason that Mom was a nurse for all those years; she loves to take care of people.

I am drawn to these types of people, especially nurses, the natural nurturers who tend to others. They care about people, truly care, and have a soothing capability that is remarkable. Mom will do anything for any one of her children, son/daughter-in-law, or grandchildren. She is my rock, but, unfortunately, she takes on too much of my worries and stress because of how much she cares. Not one day passed where my mom was not at the NICU with me.

I am the kind of person who is not 100 percent comfortable with others doing too many things for me. I always feel like I am "putting people out" if they are spending their time on me, especially if that means sitting in a hospital room listening to beeping monitors for hours on end.

But not with Mom. She wanted and needed to be there just as much as I did. I know how much it worried and hurt and pained her to see Brady in the NICU. It tore her up that her daughter was going through such a life-changing experience. She still takes on my pain and worry and somehow that comforts me. It is almost as if she is carrying part of my load. I do not feel as alone.

## MY LIFELINES

The NICU became my refuge, my family, my horror, and my place for six months.

The nurses and doctors in this small unit of Greater Baltimore Medical Center (GBMC) hospital quickly became our lifelines. The doctors were always there to patiently explain Brady's medical needs, never making us feel like their time was too valuable. We hung onto every word they uttered.

The nurses do double duty; they not only take care of the babies, they take care of the parents as well. They were constantly looking out for us, encouraging us to take breaks, get a bite to eat, or rest when Brady was having a stable couple of hours. We truly became family to each other, talking for hours about our personal lives and experiences outside the NICU.

Katie was our adorable twenty-five-year-old night nurse who, despite her age, had the air of a truly seasoned nurse. She always called me "Mom" and Brady was "her boyfriend."

"Mom, go home. You know I will call you if anything happens. He will be fine," she would tell me. I needed those gentle words of encouragement to leave the hospital every night and try to get some sleep in my own bed. Katie never minded my multiple nightly phone calls to check in, and she always tried to put me at ease when Brady was in her care.

I liked Katie so much that after we "graduated" from the NICU, I asked her if I could give my single cousin her phone number. I was thinking these two millennials would hit it off, and I was always looking for a good successful setup. She said yes. About six months had passed and I asked my cousin Chris how it was going.

His reply: "Great, we text every day."

"Text every day?" I yelled at him. "Um, How about picking up the phone? Texting is not a relationship last time I checked?"

I found out that they hadn't even talked on the phone! Say what? Mackey quickly told Chris to stop dicking around and call her. He said, "We give you a layup like this, an awesome girl and a nurse and this is how you operate?" Mackey jokes.

Chris and Katie met at Starbucks that next day and got married two years later.

Brady's main nurses during the day were Bev and Judy. Bev was a sweetheart of a woman with a gentle and quiet nature. She was the most positive person in the NICU. She was quick to make a joke and have a laugh. It brightened my day every time I walked in and saw that she was on shift and would be my company for those long hours.

The day finally came when I was able to do Kangaroo Care with Brady. Bev ever so gently placed him on my chest, then regularly remarked how well he was doing now that he was skin-to-skin with his mama. Bev's attitude and positivity allowed me to actually picture a future with my baby. In those early days she reassured me by saying quite naturally, "When he turns one" or "He's going to give you trouble as a teenager!" She believed in him and never lost faith. For this, I will always be indebted to her. I realized that the other nurses and doctors did not want to get our hopes up by talking about the months to come, but I have learned that positive thinking is pretty much everything, and Bev had perfected that art.

---

Judy was our other day shift nurse, and she was also with us the day that Jud passed. She was a woman I instantly picked out as the most seasoned and experienced nurse in the unit. All the other nurses came to her for advice on their patients, asked her to start IV lines in their babies' tiny little veins, and generally looked up to her as a veteran.

I immediately befriended her and requested her whenever she was on shift. She also took a liking to Brady, and he became "her" baby. I think she also liked the tough cases, the extreme preemies, and Brady fit the bill.

Judy, in fact, actually saved Brady's life. When Brady was twenty-five days old, he was not having a good day. His required oxygen levels had been climbing steadily all morning long, and he was quickly reaching 80 percent oxygen. As I mentioned, the highest a ventilator could go was 100 percent; after that his lungs could collapse.

Suddenly he needed 90 percent and then 100 percent. The nurses and doctors quickly came in to assess the situation. They could give him steroids to strengthen his lungs, but there could be serious side effects, including brain bleeds and cerebral palsy. And there was no guarantee that the steroids would work. The doctor on call was hesitant to administer the steroids and instead ordered more and more tests to see what the root of the problem was. Yet each new test required more poking and prodding, which in turn put stress on Brady and his lungs. What he needed was to be left alone. It was a catch-22.

After hearing the game plan of more tests being ordered, Judy stepped in and told the doctors that Brady needed a course of steroids immediately.

"What does it matter if he develops cerebral palsy if he doesn't make it alive to see tomorrow?" she basically yelled at the doctors. They discussed their strategy and, after a lot of back and forth, decided to listen to Judy. After all, didn't Brady's nurse know him better than anyone in the unit?

The steroids were given. Judy instructed everyone to please leave the room immediately after. She urged the doctors to not do any more testing. She turned the lights down and placed her healing hands on Brady's head and under his bottom and sat there for a long time. His oxygen levels quickly began to drop, and you could physically see him starting to relax and grow more comfortable. Judy's calming nature and overall love for Brady during his NICU stay meant everything to us. To this day, she still watches the kids every time we go away for an extended period.

During the first four months of Brady's life in the NICU, bringing him home was not an option ever discussed by the doctors. The daily conversations revolved around what could be done to keep him alive. We literally took it one day at a time. Our only goal: KEEP HIM ALIVE. But as we made it into the end of his fifth month of his hospitalization, the conversation evolved, and we could sense that we were entering a safe zone. *Would* we ever get to bring him home changed to *when* we bring him home. Our little angel Jud was doing his job up in heaven.

# 15

# LACEY: THE UNEXPECTED

During Milly's first month at home, Ben and I were in full-on parent mode and loving every waking (and sleeping) second of it. I looked forward to my daily five-mile walks with Milly around the Naval Academy followed by coffee at the Annapolis market, where everyone commented on how great I looked after just having a baby (at some point I just stopped reiterating the entire story and said, "Thanks!").

Milly and I both loved the fresh air and our daily outings, with me staring at her the entire time we strolled. I still could not believe she was mine and did not want to take my eyes off her for even a second. It was the first time in four years that I felt whole again.

Around two weeks after Milly was born, we planned a road trip to our alma mater, the University of Virginia. Our purpose was twofold: to attend a gala event in honor of Milly's paternal grandpa and to take Milly to her first UVA football game. Ben is an avid fan of UVA basketball and football, to put it lightly. As we were driving south on Route 29, I asked Ben to stop at a convenience store for a quick bathroom break and some snacks. Even though I wasn't breastfeeding, taking care of another human had made me much hungrier lately, and I had guzzled around 100 ounces of water.

When I entered the 7-Eleven restroom, something seemed off. Was I accidentally peeing in my pants? No, to my surprise, there was blood in my underwear! Despite the fact that most women dread this time of the month, after not having a natural period for fourteen years, it felt like I had just hit the jackpot. It was truly miraculous from my perspective.

Holding Milly, cuddling her day and night, napping daily with her, kangarooing her to my body, studying her for hours on end, feeding her all day and night; all of this must have reset my hormones and changed my body. I had heard stories like this before, but now I was experiencing it firsthand.

———————

After a few sleepless weeks, Ben and I were thrilled to have Milly home with us, and we lived in a constant state of bliss. I had a strange feeling that something was different and had a weird premonition that my body was changing. Around two weeks after our trip to Charlottesville and my surprise period, I went downstairs one night and announced to Ben, "I think I'm ovulating."

Ben was taken aback and asked, "Is that even possible?"

"Well," I replied, "it's either that or there's egg white in my underwear."

Without wasting any time, I dashed out the door to Rite Aid to buy an ovulation kit. This was my hundredth ovulation test, and I had spent quite a bit of money on them. My intuition was correct, and the test confirmed that I was indeed ovulating. I couldn't believe it. This was nothing short of a miracle. I immediately told Ben that we had to seize this opportunity and try on our own. Get your ass upstairs, Ben!

Two more weeks passed, making it six weeks since Milly's birth, and we decided to celebrate Ben's birthday by heading to DC. We had been constantly taking care of Milly since bringing her home, but we decided it was time for us to sneak away for two hours to celebrate. We left Milly with her grandparents, while we ventured out for a quick dinner. We went to one of our favorite restaurants in Georgetown, Peacock Cafe, where in years past we were known to indulge in numerous drinks to get the night started. Yet, this night was different from the past nights. I ordered a ginger ale and a loaf of bread, which surprised Ben as I usually enjoyed some type of fruity cocktails on a night out.

In the back of my mind, I had been tracking my menstrual cycle since ovulating and having sex, assuming that I would have gotten my period a few days prior. However, that time came and went, and somewhere deep within, I began to feel a glimmer of hope that I might have conceived. I didn't want to say anything to Ben and put false hope in his mind since he was already so happy with Milly, and it could have been too much too soon.

During dinner, I casually mentioned to Ben that I had not gotten my period and had been feeling more tired than usual. However, he didn't think much of it since I had been up every night with Milly, while he had been away in Dallas for work all week. I decided to keep these thoughts to myself and told myself that if I didn't get my period by Monday, I would take a pregnancy test.

The next day was Sunday and Ben boarded his weekly flight to Dallas late that night. At the time, Ben was a prosecutor for the Department of Justice and spent his weekdays trying cases in Texas. I woke up early that Monday morning, still no period in sight. I fastened Milly into her stroller and walked immediately to Rite Aid. I bought the most expensive pregnancy test I could find (I was worried the dollar-store ones I had at home would not suffice) and went home to take it.

It was not my earliest morning urine, which those tests recommend using, so I was worried that there may be insufficient hCG in my urine to measure an early pregnancy. But I was not waiting one more day, so mid-morning urine would have to do.

After taking the pregnancy test, I left it in the bathroom and went downstairs to sit on the couch with my baby girl. I tried to calm myself and be realistic about the situation. However, I couldn't help but talk to Milly, sharing my deepest hopes and dreams with her. For once, I felt relaxed taking a pregnancy test. But deep down, I had a strong feeling about this one.

After waiting the suggested five minutes, Milly and I went back upstairs to the bathroom. That's when we were greeted with two of the biggest, boldest, and most prominent pink lines ever. I immediately lifted Milly up in the air and gave her a big kiss while tears of joy streamed down my face. I thanked her for being my miracle baby and for changing our lives so profoundly. Milly was the angel who made my dreams of becoming a mother and having a big family possible. She was my living proof that miracles do happen.

After relishing this moment with Milly, I took a picture of us—me holding her with the pregnancy test resting on her belly—and texted it to Ben.

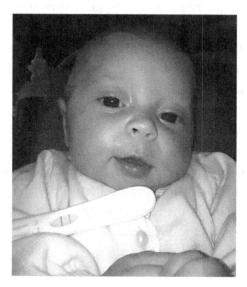

Milly holding the positive pregnancy test.

"Huh?" was his return text followed up by an immediate call. "Wait, Lace, what is that?" He could not believe it, he was stunned. I mean truly floored; he actually thought I was pranking him. I explained to him that I had an odd feeling that I was pregnant over the last few days but did not want to jinx it so I kept it to myself. After a conversation full of shock and more shock (sorry, but no other way to describe it), we got off the phone and I called Dr. Mottla. I could not wait to tell him about my unbelievable luck, that I did this on my own. He was so happy for us, but absolutely dumbfounded as well. He told me to come into his office for a blood test to confirm, which I did immediately. He wasted no time and put me on progesterone to help thicken my lining, just in case.

Those first few weeks of being pregnant were a bit of a nauseous blur. The only thing that alleviated my constant nausea was cold Coke and bacon/egg/cheese sandwiches. I was waking every three hours to feed Milly while feeling exhausted from being pregnant. We napped daily in my bed together while our daily coffee runs and five-mile walks became a thing of the past. Instead we would leave the house after our morning nap and head out in search of the biggest hoagie or Italian cold cut that we could find.

All was going well and progressing as normal until I woke up one morning with blood in my underwear. Milly and I had been staying at my parents' house while Ben was in Dallas. Being a single mom was tough. Being a single mom to a newborn and pregnant in my first trimester was doubly as tough. Mama needed some help from the grandparents.

In my childhood bathroom that morning, my heart was in my throat as I processed everything. I immediately said a prayer to God, begging him for this baby to be okay. I called the doctor, grabbed my keys, and got right in the car to head back to Annapolis for an ultrasound.

Upon arrival, I was whisked back to an examining room and hooked up to a monitor. "Thump, thump, thump, thump," I heard

my baby's heartbeat immediately and cried tears of utter gratitude. Dr. Mottla explained to me that I had a placenta hematoma,
like Becky's, and while the blood was scary to see, it was not af-
fecting the baby at all. He hoped that within a few days the spotting would subside . . . and it did. It seemed as if I was following in
Becky's footsteps with this one.

And so began the healthy and mostly uncomplicated pregnancy of my second child, a beautiful baby boy. Robert Benjamin
O'Neil, or Bo for short, was born on August 20, 2012—just ten
months and ten days after Milly's arrival. Appropriately named
after his strong grandfathers, Bo came into this world in the most
unexpected yet welcoming way. We never dreamed we would be
lucky enough to see this day. And I had to thank my little Milly
for her perfect timing. She crawled for the first time on the eve of
her baby brother's birth. Whether she was ready or not, she must
have sensed my fear that I would miss her first crawl while I was
in the hospital giving birth. I'd waited too long and come too far
to miss any of her big milestones.

Wow, what a difference a year can make; we had quickly become a family of four in less than eleven months. Life with "Irish
Twins" was hectic and exhausting, and I loved every damn minute
of it. Mine and Ben's dreams of having a large family were unfolding right before our eyes. My belief that things would work out in
the end was finally proving true.

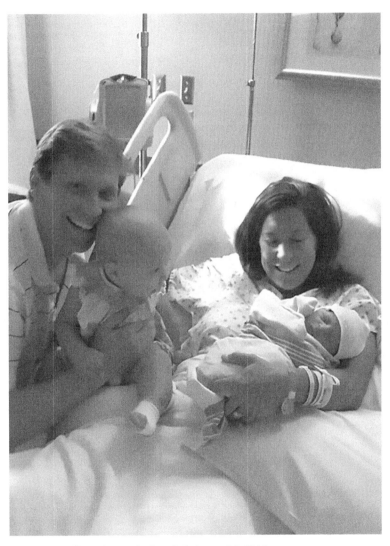

Lacey, Ben, Milly, and Bo in the hospital, August 20, 2012.

# 16

# LAUREN: BRADY'S HOMECOMING

After close to six months of pure hell in the neonatal intensive care unit, Mackey and I brought Brady home. Finally.

Lacey and Mom threw a last-minute baby shower for me the day before the homecoming, and people came out in droves to celebrate. That is what you get when you live in your hometown—a hell of a lot of support. While I had barely seen anyone for the last six months, I could feel the love from my town and it filled me with gratitude.

I will admit that I have the occasional bitch session about living back in Baltimore, just a mile away from where I grew up. Living on the coast or mountains would be so much better and so fitting for our active family. The bottom line, however, is that we are fortunate to have a huge extended family and group of friends to live alongside.

When Brady was in the NICU, it felt like every person I had ever known was either writing us letters, dropping off dinners, saying prayers for us at Sunday Mass, or simply reaching out to our family members to see how we were holding up. Both my and Mackey's immediate families were there for us every single day, rooting for Brady and taking care of the two of us. The love that they surrounded us with is truly remarkable. That, my friends, is why we live in Baltimore. Having both of our families here with us during this period of utter turbulence felt like a shield of armor. The amount of support we received still humbles me years later.

I had already been out of work for seven months at this point—one month on bedrest and then six months in the NICU. My wonderful company agreed to give me an additional three months off now that Brady was home. Truly amazing. I was actually going to have a "normal" maternity leave, a time to welcome our son home.

Lauren, Mackey, and Brady, the day of discharge from the NICU, June 15, 2012.

Brady Boy was finally coming home, but there was a caveat. He would be on supplemental oxygen 24/7. He could not survive without a constant supply of oxygen via nasal cannula (tube), and so began my next profession as an at-home healthcare aide in many ways (minus the whole nursing school thing again which I am preeeeettty sure is important).

When I think back on it now, this whole idea seems insane. It seemed that way eight years ago as well, but I was so damn excited to have him home that I glazed over it. Caring for a child on oxygen means that you have their life in your hands. Every. Single. Moment. What if the cannula falls out or slips to the side of his nostrils, or the tank isn't working properly and while the gauge is reading that there is enough oxygen, there actually isn't? What if you turn your back for a minute and the baby has ripped the cord out of the tank (which does happen)? He needed this supplemental oxygen every moment of his life, and we were responsible to make sure he had it. Thinking about it even now makes me feel sick.

## OUR HOME LOOKS LIKE A HOSPITAL

The day before Brady's arrival we had a home healthcare company deliver five gigantic oxygen tanks along with other equipment: tubing, supplies, extra tank parts, monitors. The overworked respiratory therapist gave us a quick thirty-minute spiel on "how to operate an oxygen tank," in other words, "keeping a human being alive," and then the tech tried to skedaddle out of the house. I nearly punched him in the face.

"Wait, whoaaaaa there, Mister," I said. "How do I know if the oxygen is on? I mean, I get that you turn this knob, but you can't hear anything. There is no on button that lights up. What if it's faulty or something?"

The therapist dryly replied, "You will know because your son will turn blue if it's not."

Sweet, thanks, asshole. "Hmm, okay, and how do I walk around the house with him if his oxygen tank weighs fifty pounds?"

The guy was unmoved. "See the forty-foot tubing?" he said dispassionately. "Just tow it behind you."

I was not going to give up. "And how do I refill the tanks once they get low?"

Practically out the door, he replied, "Call our office and we can hopefully have it out to you in twenty-four hours or so, but it might take longer."

Was he trying to teach me how to cook a chicken pot pie, or keep my son from going into respiratory failure? What I needed was a week of intensive instruction followed by a written exam and then a few simulated test drives to make sure I could do this. Stressful? Um, yes, I'd say so.

We had three hulking oxygen tanks that sat on each floor of our house. We would carry Brady around, trying not to trip on his mile-long nasal cannula tube. When we did leave the house, we carried a smaller oxygen tank that slung like a backpack over our shoulders. (He ended up staying on oxygen until the age of two because his lungs were still not fully developed.)

Along with his oxygen tank, Brady arrived home on eleven different medications, which had to be given three times a day. We had to give him a nebulizer of a steroid, albuterol, six times a day, each one lasting for about fifteen minutes. He was hooked up to a heart monitor that falsely alarmed every five minutes or so. While he was taking some bottles of breast milk, he also had a feeding tube. His lungs were not yet strong enough to be able to feed six times a day, which is what he needed to get the proper nutrition.

Each bottle took him forty minutes to consume because we had to feed him slowly so that he wouldn't aspirate, or have milk enter his airway. We always wanted him to get the full bottle in, but you also couldn't tire him out too much with his feeds. It was a balancing act. Once he was done, there was a 60 to 70 percent chance that the whole bottle was coming right back up as his belly was still so sensitive. Milk spit-up was splattered everywhere—the house, our cars, and every article of clothing we wore.

Our bedroom, where Brady slept, looked more like an intensive care unit than a place of rest. There were IV poles, a constant tangle of lines and wires, and incessant beeping of machines and monitors. That didn't stop Mackey and me from making this seem like normal life. We were elated to have our boy home and nothing else mattered whatsoever. Life was good despite these challenges, and we felt blessed and lucky. So lucky. When I was feeling overwhelmed, I reminded myself (daily) that there is always, always, someone who has it worse. I counted my blessings.

The first couple of months at home with our little Brady, while grueling, were amazing. Life was good. Life was great, actually. My little man had survived, and we were able to begin our life with our first child. Despite that feeling of peace, my mind took me down rabbit holes of worry from time to time. Would Brady develop normally, would he walk, eat on his own, have cerebral palsy, learn to talk? We didn't know and neither did the doctors. It was a wait-and-see game, but Mackey and I agreed that whatever came his way, we could handle it. Nothing at this point was life-threatening and that was all that mattered.

---

While we had made it out of the hospital, our days were constantly filled with check-ups and doctor's appointments in those first few months. We spent countless hours with our pulmonologist, developmental specialists, and feeding-clinic nurses. Occupational therapists and physical therapists checked in biweekly. My pediatrician was on speed dial and still to this day remains a very special person to our family.

But on August 11, we would go to the one appointment that would rock our world: Brady's hearing check-up.

Brady had failed his newborn hearing test in the NICU right before we left for home. The doctors and nurses had assured us that this was usually the case with all preemies. Vernix (the waxy white covering that babies are born with) in the ear canal, fluid in the middle ear, or too much movement or crying from the baby can alter the test results. He would most likely be fine at his follow-up, they said.

So, on a sweltering hot day in August, Brady and I headed to Greater Baltimore Medical Center for his appointment with absolutely no worries. I told Mackey that he didn't need to be there, that I would take this one on my own.

Two audiologists came out to the waiting room and ushered us back into the hearing booth. "We are going to be performing an ABR, or Auditory Brain Response, test on Brady," said one of the doctors, quickly uncoiling and hooking up what looked like a million cords. She placed headphones over his ears and electrodes on his head while the other doctor manned the booth.

"Sounds will be played through these headphones and the electrodes will measure his brain's response to those sounds," she explained.

I nodded and didn't pay too much attention to all of the details, clearly not too worried that there would be an issue. I was told that I could sit in the room, off to the side, while they worked with him. As I sat in the corner, mindlessly scouring the internet on my phone, I occasionally glanced over to see how things were going. Brady was hooked up to a bunch of wires, and the audiologists were at their computers conducting the test. I noticed them quietly conversing many times throughout the test.

They are just discussing the logistics of the ABR, I told myself. Does one of the docs look concerned, or am I just imagining it? After about forty-five minutes, the doctor in the booth told me that they were done and asked me to come back to their office to talk. I picked up Brady and the four of us headed back.

As we sat down, I noticed immediately that they were both looking at me with pained faces. They began by asking if there was anyone else with me at the appointment, or did I come alone?

I knew right then and there that something was very wrong. I quickly replied that I was alone and asked how Brady had done on the ABR. I needed to know what they were holding back, and I needed to know fast.

The news that they delivered was devastating—Brady was deaf. Not hard of hearing, not a child with hearing loss who can hopefully wear hearing aids, but 100 percent deaf. My world came crumbling down and I absolutely lost it. My heart split in two for all of those times that I had been reading and singing and cooing to Brady in the NICU and he did not hear me. All of the times I read the book *My Mom and Me* through the incubator, thinking that I was comforting him, but I had been just silent to him.

My heart broke for him, for what he was going to have to deal with for the rest of his life, for how much harder life would be for him. And how had I not noticed? Was I too preoccupied with all of the other more life-threatening complications that could sweep in at a moment's time and carry him off? How, as his mother, did I not know? Didn't he respond to my voice when I spoke to him? Or was I just always bent over him, face to face, talking to my baby boy, not knowing that he was simply watching my facial expressions? I knew at this moment that our lives had been further changed forever.

The memory of that day will always be fresh in my mind. I will never forget the utter pain and despair that I had to work through. The guilt that I felt. He would not be deaf if my body had been strong enough to keep him in my belly. His hearing loss was most likely a side effect from all of the antibiotics that he was given in the NICU. Because of me, Brady would be saddled with a disability for the rest of his life. Life would undoubtedly be harder on him. Kids might be cruel to him. He would be different.

# WELCOME TO HOLLAND

I allowed myself a few days of incessant tears and then I kicked myself in the ass and decided that, from here on out, I would be strong for Brady. Mackey, while devastated for Brady, was incredibly optimistic and positive. He lifted me up in a way that no other person could, and I knew that with him by my side, we would be fine.

Thinking back on it now, remembering him in that moment, makes me love him even more than I thought possible. We had always said in the NICU that we could deal with anything that came our way, so long as Brady made it out of the hospital. We simply wanted him to live. Well, this was clearly our test because he was alive and the fact that he was deaf did not change things. We were simply going down a different path.

One of my favorite poems, given to me by a very dear friend, is "Welcome to Holland" by Emily Perl Kingsley. It describes the experience of raising a child with a disability. It says that when you are planning on having a baby, it is like planning a fabulous trip—to Italy. You make all of your arrangements, decide all of the amazing sites you are going to see, which restaurants you will dine in, and book the best hotels. You set off on the plane and as you touch down after a long haul, the flight attendant says, "Welcome to Holland."

Confused, you explain that you were supposed to be in Italy as that is what you have been planning all along, and all of your friends have done this trip to Italy and that is where you are supposed to be. But the flight path has changed and now you land in Holland. And although Holland is not Italy, it is still special in a different kind of way. You meet amazing people in Holland that you would not have met in Italy, and you see beautiful windmills and tulips, and life is slower paced in Holland. Holland is not what you had planned, but Holland is a true gift that changes you for the better.

Brady became our Holland.

# 17

# LAUREN: LET'S HEAR IT FOR BRADY BOY

The doctors explained that Brady might be a candidate for cochlear implants (CIs). I had never even heard of this medical device and had never met anyone with a CI. With Brady's new diagnosis, I was determined to figure out everything there was to know about this cutting-edge technology. I quickly found out that cochlear implants are literally the only device that can replicate a human sense—hearing.

After a ton of research and speaking to as many medical professionals as possible, we scheduled Brady for an appointment at the Johns Hopkins Listening Center to be evaluated for implants. We were thrilled; Hopkins was one of the top pediatric audiology centers in the country and it was less than ten miles from our house.

After his initial screenings, Hopkins told us that Brady was indeed a candidate for cochlear implants. We were over the moon. At the time, the youngest age a child could be implanted was age one, and damned if we didn't have him on the surgery schedule the day after his first birthday. He was going to have bilateral implants, meaning each ear would receive an implant. However, because of his weak lungs, the surgeons had to perform two separate surgeries.

It would have taken eight hours in surgery to implant both ears, and the doctors did not want him to be under anesthesia for that long. Brady was still on supplemental oxygen.

The first surgery went smoothly. Brady was in the operating room for about four hours. While it felt awful being back in a waiting room pacing around while sending up prayers for Brady, this time felt quite different. We were excited for what was to come.

After four tense hours, we were told to come back to the recovery unit. As I walked to his bedside, I took one look at his huge bandaged head and lost it. He looked so worn out and fragile. As he woke from the anesthesia, though, he soon smiled up at us and within three hours of getting him home later that day, he was happily playing on the floor with his toys. I had no idea how resilient kids can be.

Cochlear implant surgery is fascinating, to put it mildly. A surgeon places a receiver into the drilled-out area of the patient's skull bone and an electrode array is inserted into the cochlea. This is the internal device. You then have to wait about a month before this incision heals in order for the patient to get the external device. The external device is the piece that sits behind the ear and receives sound. It looks like a hearing aid.

So, while it was great to have the surgery behind us, the real moment of truth would arrive approximately a month after surgery, when swelling had subsided, and Brady was "activated." This is when they would turn on his external device and see if it is interacting with the internal device, thus producing sound. This would be the first time that Brady would hear.

It was February 26 as we drove to Hopkins for the activation appointment. Mackey and I were filled with nervous excitement. Both of our moms, Sue and Fifi, were with us, their never-ending support continuing with each leg of Brady's journey. We wanted them to experience this incredible moment with us. They deserved it. The questions were swirling around in all of our heads on that drive to the clinic. How would Brady react to hearing our voices? How would he adjust to this new world of his? Was the surgery a success?

Upon arrival, our audiologist, Courtney, greeted us with a huge smile. "Are you ready to hear for the first time, buddy?" she asked, smiling at Brady. "Mom and Dad, I don't need to ask if you are. I know the answer to that one." Seeing the anticipation on our faces, she ushered us all back to her office.

For the first thirty minutes, we were taught how to operate his external device, the small hook-shaped piece that would be a permanent fixture on Brady's ear. We were then told it was time to activate his implant. We all held our breaths as Courtney tapped on her computer, preparing for what was to come.

"Okay, I'm ready to turn it on. Mom, do you want to speak to him first?" she asked.

I nodded my head as a wave of nervousness washed over me. This would be the first time Brady would hear my voice, the first time he would hear anything for that matter. I softly said to Brady, "Hi, my love bug," and kissed him on the cheek. I will never forget what happened next.

Huge, silent, alligator tears rolled down his face. Brady did not utter a sound, just sat there and silently cried at this frightening new sense that was invading his, until now, silent world. The surgery had worked. This felt like a miracle to us. We sat there for an hour talking and cooing to him, letting him get used to this new phenomenon. We knew that it would be a long road ahead, filled with months and years of therapy as well as hardship, but this was truly a miraculous moment. We thanked God for all that He had done.

Brady's second surgery and activation went smoothly as well, and by the time he was a year and a half, he was bilaterally implanted and babbling up a storm.

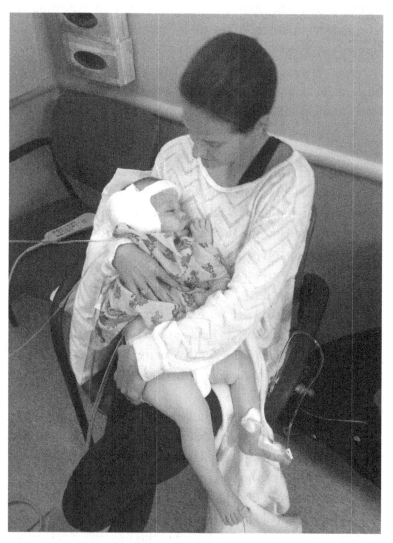

Brady postsurgery, January 2013.

From that day forward, we began navigating his new cochlear implant world, constantly working with him on his listening and speech development. A cochlear implant provides sound, but it doesn't give the wearer 100 percent natural hearing. You are essentially working with fewer "tools in your toolbox," and there is a huge learning curve to listening and processing that sound. Every minute of every day we worked with him to build auditory skills and understand this new range of sounds. He seemed to be progressing daily, his baby brain rapidly absorbing each bit of new information. We felt so fortunate for this incredible technology.

Immediately after the implantation, we were introduced to Kim Kiernan and Kathy Lenhert, two women who would change our lives as well as Brady's.

Kim was a speech therapist who knew every doctor, nurse, therapist, and speech pathologist who had anything to do with cochlear implants. Her wealth of knowledge and experience in the field was absolutely overwhelming. From the moment we met, she became like family. And Brady was her boy. They bonded immediately and she loved him like her own. She also became my sounding board for all things Brady related—not just in terms of his implants, but for everything. She became like a second mother to me and lifted me up when I needed it.

Her twice weekly meetings at our home became the highlight of my week. She taught me the best lesson I had learned yet. "Throw out all those special needs, deafness, preemie categories," she would say. "He's Brady. He's just Brady and everyone will love him for who he is."

My God, no one could have spoken truer words. This is truly what every parent who has a child with special needs should be told. We, as parents, get so caught up in defining our children and figuring out how to diagnose and help them that we often lose sight of the fact that they are simply and uniquely themselves. We do not need to label or categorize them but instead acknowledge their one-of-a-kind perfectness.

Kathy, who worked at the Johns Hopkins Listening Center, was Brady's speech pathologist. The center is in charge of working with recently implanted children to teach them how to listen. Learning to listen is the first step in learning to speak. Kathy is an unbelievably kind, intelligent, warm person who loves what she does. I could tell by the way she looked at Brady how much love she had for him. Not a session went by that she didn't comment on how bright or smart he was, how he was a super star with his implants. We met with her every Monday afternoon for three straight years. She gave us the tools to help Brady maximize the benefits that a cochlear implant can provide.

Kim and Kathy helped us navigate both the hardware of the cochlear implants as well as the many therapies that would benefit Brady. These two angels came into his life and changed his path forward. They became his cheerleaders. Perhaps more importantly, they became the support system that Mackey and I needed to navigate this new world of ours. Once again, just like the nurses in the NICU, we found truly amazing tour guides who taught us to find our way around "Holland."

Despite all of this, I still had daily tears of frustration and worry. How would Brady continue to develop? Would he gain weight? Would he go to school eventually? Would he learn to walk on his own? The stress was endless.

I was constantly comparing him to the many kids we knew who were his age. I recognized that this was extremely unfair, but it was hard to stop. I knew that he shouldn't be hitting his milestones at the same time as these other babies, but it still was like a punch in the gut with each one that he missed. Every month that went by, he lagged further behind. I felt so scared for what the future would hold for him, for how hard life could potentially be for him and our family if Brady didn't reach key milestones.

On top of all of this, the loss of Jud haunted me every moment of every day. I should have been caring for two babies, not one. I felt his loss with every motherly duty that I performed.

# 18

# LAUREN:
# THAT'S MY GIRL

When Brady was just ten months old, I decided it was time for another baby. I say "I" because Mack thought I was a certified lunatic for wanting another child with all that we currently had going on.

Well, just about everyone, besides Lacey, thought I was bat shit. I was recently back to work full-time, having secured one of the greatest nannies of all-time, a soft-spoken woman named Alice. She had been in childcare her entire life and the confidence with which she took on Brady and his complicated care was inspiring. She loved him in a way that a grandmother loves a grandchild and constantly was working with him to reach his milestones. This angel stayed with our family for the next six years.

Brady was in constant therapies: occupational, physical, feeding clinics. The doctors' appointments were never ending and seemed to take up all of our free time. Nonetheless, we had always wanted a large family, and I knew that whatever challenges in life

Brady would have, a sibling that was close in age to him would only push him to overcome those challenges and be his ally along the way. I was operating from a "strength in numbers" kind of mentality. It was time for another baby.

I scheduled an appointment with my ob-gyn, Dr. K, to see what my options were and to discuss the situation. He had barely sat down in his chair when I blurted out, "Okay, so I want another baby."

He looked at me like I had ten heads, took a breath, and in his very direct, matter-of-fact manner, explained: "Lauren, you got to twenty-four weeks gestation with twins. Now I think I can get you to twenty-eight weeks with a singleton, but with your incompetent cervix, I cannot be entirely sure."

Um, say what, doc? "Twenty-eight weeks? Well, Dr. K, twenty-eight weeks means the NICU and I cannot go back there."

"And bedrest will most likely be in your future as well," he added, only crushing me further.

When I heard all of this, I felt light-headed. I did not foresee this, did not realize that my cervix could be incompetent with a singleton as well. Mack and I weighed our options, and we decided that our best path, for this pregnancy, would be adoption or surrogacy.

Lacey had paved the road of surrogacy for me. She had already had Milly and her experience with Becky could not have been more perfect. When it came to surrogacy experiences, theirs was a fairytale.

After my demoralizing appointment with Dr. K, Lacey listened to my fears and confidently said, "Well then, we know what you need to do. Ask Becky."

"What do you mean ask Becky?" I fired back, taking some of my frustration out on her unjustly. "We both know that Becky is done having babies. She said so after Milly was born. She's done."

"Yes, she did say that she was done, but what is the harm in reaching out?"

At this point, Becky had carried three of her own children and had delivered three surrogate babies (a set of twins and Milly). We both doubted that her doctor would even allow her to have another C-section, but I have always lived by the motto "if you don't ask, you will never know."

On a rainy Tuesday in November, Becky and I met for lunch; we had decided to meet at a deli near her house. As I walked into the restaurant, I will never forget how nervous she looked. Looking back on this moment, I feel the full weight of her nerves. She knew why I had reached out to her. I was going to ask this incredible woman to carry and deliver her seventh child. No wonder she looked stricken.

My impatient ass was barely in the chair when words started spewing from my mouth. Would she ever do another surrogacy? Is it even possible? "I'm very easy to work with," I promised her, acting like she was interviewing me for a sales job. "I won't bother you at all, seriously, I probably won't even check in that much!"

Luckily, Becky has a very calming way about her, a complete juxtaposition to my unrestrained awkward word vomit.

"Honestly, Lauren," she said, after she'd heard me out, "I've been lucky enough to have six uncomplicated births and my time is probably done."

My body went weak, I could feel the pull of the earth's gravity weighing me down. This woman had been pregnant five times. That's 200 weeks of pregnancy in her lifetime. What was I even thinking asking her?

I grabbed the waiter by the arm and ordered a beer. I wanted to disappear. Becky gently grabbed my hands from across the table. She held them tightly as she admitted that she felt nauseous on her way to meet me for lunch. That made two of us.

"I told myself the only way I would ever consider becoming a surrogate again was if there was a person who was truly in need," she said. "Lacey told me your story, and you are that person."

The world went dark for a minute, and I froze. Did she just say what I thought she said? Tears dropped from my eyes. Gratitude can be the most powerfully humbling feeling in the entire world. I lunged awkwardly across the table and hugged Becky as I sobbed, soaking her hair with my tears. If the doctors would allow it, Becky would give me this life-changing gift.

Mackey and I set up a meeting with Peggy Swain, Lacey's attorney. I knew that employing a lawyer was step one. We then had to see if Becky was able to carry another pregnancy. As we walked into her OB's office just a few weeks later, my stomach was in knots. Would this really be feasible?

"So you really want to do this again?" the doctor asked, unbelieving.

Becky nodded her head and smiled at me. I was completely blown away by her courage. The OB said that despite so many pregnancies, Becky's uterus was in great condition and that we could move forward. Step two, check. We were ready to formally begin the process.

Now let's stop here. I'd like to say that I fully realized that my path to getting a surrogate was quite possibly the easiest road to travel of any fertility-challenged gal out there. I almost feel ashamed when I tell people how quickly and with such ease this process unfolded. But then I remember how much I went through to get to this moment. I have been asked by so many people for advice on finding a surrogate and I am usually very honest with them. It was super easy for me. Like annoyingly easy. I simply went and asked Becky. Lacey had truly done all of the hard work. She was the one who originally found Becky.

Becky and I decided to use Shady Grove Fertility in Baltimore to guide us in the IVF process. Our doctor, Dr. Y, was a small, soft-spoken man from Chile. I loved his accent and his sense of humor, which so often came out right when I needed it.

"Lauren, you calm down now and don't worry," he'd say. "We are working with the best uterus in the house."

As Becky began to get ready and cleared for the implantation process, I began yet another stimulation period in hopes of producing some quality follicles. Unfortunately, I did not have any frozen embryos from my last IVF retrieval with Brady and Jud.

I went in for my egg retrieval on a snowy Wednesday morning feeling great. Why was I feeling so great? Because I already had a child. The stress that I had felt in the past to "just have a baby, just one" was so overwhelming when I started the IVF process in 2009. The thoughts of *Will I ever have a child or be a mother or have a family?* were constantly whirling in my brain and the possibility of not having those things scared the ever-living crap out of me. But I had my baby Brady at home, I was already a mom. That stress was gone.

Once you have that first baby in your life, and you have officially become a mom, the tidal wave of stress that once loomed over you all but washes away. Sure, you are worried that you may not be able to have another one, but that worry is insignificant compared to the thought of never having children. And don't get me wrong, there is absolutely nothing wrong with never having children. Many people choose this road, and damn does their life look good! But these people refer to themselves as child-free; whereas, those who want to have children and can't, think of themselves as childless.

When you are going through infertility and IVF, when all you want is to have your first baby, the fear of being childless is what keeps you up at night. Then once you have a child, you begin to worry about other things: their health, development, everyday chores of feeding and raising and caring for a baby. Your mind is constantly scheduling and planning and thinking about that to-do list. There isn't much time to worry about the other one coming down the pike because the one you have right now is a hell of a lot of work.

You also, for some stupid reason, feel as if you are now a part of that sacred sorority of mothers. You are right there with your other friends, doing playdates, attending first birthday parties, and bitching about the lack of sleep. You proudly wear that

Babybjorn around your neck like a badge of honor. You finally feel at peace. At least for me it was that way.

# BACK TO REALITY

After retrieving seventeen eggs, we were left with eight good embryos that were fertilized by Mackey's sperm. I had never had such incredible numbers. My part was done, and damn did it feel good. We decided to transfer one grade A embryo into Becky's uterus about a month later. The transfer was pretty underwhelming, as they usually tend to be. We all watched as Dr. Y transferred our one embryo via catheter into Becky's womb and placed it in the wall of her uterus. She was then told to go home and take it relatively easy for the rest of the day. The procedure took all of ten minutes.

After twelve days of waiting, Becky went in for her hCG test, and we found out that the embryo had not implanted; she was not pregnant. She felt terrible and I felt terrible that she felt terrible. I mean, clearly it wasn't her fault. I, for one, was not deterred.

"We'll get the next one, girl!" I was loving this new role of mine as coach rather than player. Luckily, our second transfer, about two months later, resulted in a positive pregnancy test. We were ecstatic.

When Becky was roughly eight weeks along, I got a call from her late one night. My heart stopped when I saw her number flash across the screen. *This couldn't be good.* We didn't usually have late-night gossip sessions.

"Lauren, don't freak out, but I am bleeding," she calmly told me. I can still hear her now, her soothing voice not giving way to the panic that I knew she was feeling. She knew I had been down this road before. The old fear and anxiety crashed over me once again. How could this happen?

We were able to get in to see the doctor that very next day. Thankfully, as before, the ultrasound showed that it was a subchorionic hematoma that was causing the bleeding. As with most cases, the hematoma went away on its own, and Becky went on to have a fairly non-eventful first and second trimester. I had the luxury of rarely worrying about the pregnancy. I went to all of the check-ups, and we texted here and there about how she was doing, but that was it.

I was not needy, to say the least. I trusted this woman implicitly. I didn't stress over what she ate, or whether she was exercising, or how much activity she was undertaking on a daily basis. I simply let her do her job. This is the wonderful thing about surrogacy. You get to sit in the passenger seat and have someone else take the wheel. I was only able to do this because of the faith that I had in Becky. Faith that she was taking care of my baby as she would her own.

I did not feel ashamed or "less than" that someone else was carrying my child. I did not freak out over the lack of control. It's the telltale sign that you have picked the right surrogate. You trust your choice wholeheartedly and know they will handle the driving. And isn't it nice to be driven around in an Uber sometimes?

For me, the daily stress that I would have had each and every day of that pregnancy was too much for me to handle at that point in time. I gladly handed the job over to her. I also did not worry about Becky getting too attached. She had three amazing children of her own, and as she once joked to me, "I don't think I can handle another, Lauren." She was busy enough with her own family. I knew that she only thought of the baby as mine and not as belonging to her in any way, shape, or form.

"I'm just your oven," she'd say.

At thirty-four weeks' gestation, Becky called me in a slight panic and told me that she was having some pretty substantial contractions.

"Okay," I said, "we are all good. Not to worry." To me, thirty-four weeks seemed so far along. That baby was probably cooked to a well-done perfection, right? I was able to keep calm.

We met at labor and delivery forty-five minutes later and the nurses confirmed that she was dilated a few centimeters. Say what? Okay, I know I said I was calm before, but I wasn't actually ready for this child to come today. This was not how this process was supposed to go down, for the love of God! I was supposed to be getting a full-term chubster out of this surrogacy, not another visit to the NICU.

After much back and forth between the doctors, we were told that Becky could stay in the hospital on bedrest, and they would try to hold off labor for at least a few days. In this type of situation, a doctor must consider both the health of the baby and the mother. Yes, the baby would be considered premature at this point if she were to deliver. But babies born at thirty-four weeks usually have the same long-term health outcomes as those born full-term.

Of greater concern was Becky's health. Now that she had gone into preterm labor, she was more susceptible to infection and possible uterine rupture. This was, after all, her sixth pregnancy, and because of that, we had to factor in the strength of her uterus.

Because she seemed to be stable at the moment and her amniotic fluid level was still normal, the doctors felt that it was the right decision to try to hold off labor for the next few days. This would give the baby critical extra time in the womb to develop. I was beyond grateful for this. More time in the belly meant significantly less time in the NICU.

Oh, but poor Becky. She had three young kids at home who needed taking care of. She had not planned for this. Her husband, Greg, was wonderful, juggling everything while also bringing her kids to the hospital to visit. I felt so guilty having her stay on bedrest, but at the same time I was not eager to have another preterm baby.

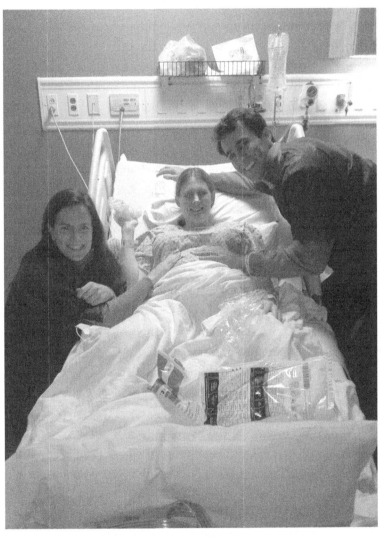

Lauren (from left), Becky, and Mackey at the hospital, December 10, 2013.

# SWEET CAROLINE

At thirty-five weeks and two days, on December 12, my sweet Caroline was born. We had decided not to find out the sex of the baby, so the day of delivery was exhilarating to say the least. Judy, Brady's nurse from the NICU, was in the delivery room with us.

Becky was having a C-section, and as the doctor pulled the baby from Becky's belly, Mackey yelled, "It's another boy!" We all cheered and screamed.

But then Judy jumped in and quickly said, "No, it's a girl, Mackey!"

Mackey had seen the umbilical cord and thought it was the penis. He clearly thinks highly of his genes, that's for sure. When I realized that I had a baby girl, my heart pretty much jumped out of my chest. The high I felt was euphoric. I would get to have that mother/daughter relationship that I was so fortunate to have with my mom. Brady would have a sister. A true partner in crime. I felt so unbelievably blessed at this moment in time and thanked God for this wonderful little angel.

Caroline Mary Cronin came into this world with a head full of blond wispy hair. She looked so delicate and feminine from the start, with a perfect little nose, large blue eyes, and a calm manner. Because she was having episodes of bradycardia, a common occurrence in preemies that causes their hearts to beat too slowly, she had to stay in the NICU for twelve days.

Ironically enough, our Brady rarely experienced bradycardia while in the NICU. Caroline's NICU stay was the polar opposite of Brady's. We were now the parents that I had looked on with envy when Brady was there, who had a "feeder and grower" baby that was simply taking a few days to develop before they were discharged. We were reunited with all of our old friends working in the unit, and it felt more like a reunion than a hospital stay.

We brought Caroline home on Christmas Eve, 2013. I could not take my eyes off this sweet little thing. We loved her blond

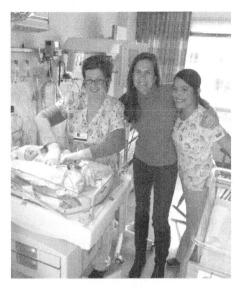

Nurse Judy (from left), Lauren, and nurse Katie
with Caroline in the NICU, December 2013.

hair and blue eyes, such a contrast to everyone else in our family
with brown hair and olive skin. Here we had this child, biologically ours to the core, but born via surrogate, who came out looking more like the surrogate than her parents! Everyone knew we
had used a gestational carrier, and after one look at this Swedish
looking babe, I could tell people's minds were reeling.

I wish I had a dollar for every time I had to explain my way
through this one. It went something like this: "Yes, she was born
via surrogate, or the correct terminology is actually gestational
carrier. Biologically she is our child—our egg and sperm—but we
needed a better oven to let this little one cook in, and Becky was
that oven."

I often think back to that first meeting when Becky agreed to
be my surrogate. She had said that her pregnancies were pretty
straightforward and easy, that if she could give someone else such
a huge gift and at the same time provide additional income for her
family, why not. In her amazing and selfless way, she was acting as
if I was doing her a favor as well.

I remember visiting Becky a year later at her new house. She and her family had moved in not long before and the kids were running around showing us their new digs, full of energy and excitement. Becky gave me the most wonderful gift ever, and at the same time she also was able to do things in her life because of the surrogacy, like help provide a new home for her family. It made me so happy because it didn't feel like a complete one-way street anymore.

The surrogacy had changed both of our lives—albeit mine more significantly than hers—for the better. To this day, Becky is always my first early morning incoming phone call on December 12, with happy birthday wishes. And my immediate response is always to thank her for giving me the most precious gift ever.

Brady and Caroline at home together for the first time, December 2013.

# 19

# LACEY: AND THEN THERE WERE SIX O'NEILS

After Bo's second birthday and right before Milly's third birthday, we decided we wanted to try for more children. It was September 2014, and I finally believed in my ability to get pregnant and the renewed strength of my body. I also had a keen understanding of my hormones at this point.

After talking with my doctor about wanting to conceive again, she decided that we should try high doses of both clomid and progesterone. Now that my body had carried a pregnancy and was in a better place, we hoped that this protocol would work. And we were right; as luck would have it, I became pregnant with my third child one month into trying. Seems impossible, right? How was I so fortunate to be one of those people who got pregnant immediately? The only real answer I could point to was Milly. I knew that after her birth something shifted inside of me, and I was forever changed. An underlying stress that I could never control evaporated the day she came into this world.

On May 28, 2015, Phoebe Myers O'Neil arrived, happily making us a family of five. Her two older siblings were ecstatic about her arrival and treated her like their own little baby doll. From the first time I looked at her, I pictured her as a "Phoebe." The meaning of the name being "bright, shining star." That is exactly what she was to all of us. Three kids under three. Bring it on!

Milly and Bo holding their new sister, Phoebe, on May 28, 2015.

Time flew from then on and life was pretty busy. I stopped working to care for my three babies at home. We were completely overwhelmed as all parents of three are; we were finally outnumbered and we loved it. But as the years flew by, I still did not feel that our family was complete. I discussed having a fourth baby with Ben, and he was on board to try. The funny thing about infertility, at least in Lauren's and my case, is that there is a place inside you that constantly yearns for more babies. After being told "no" and "sorry" so many times, there is a bottomless feeling of always wanting more of what you could not have for so long.

Yet I knew that this wasn't me just being greedy and wanting to conquer a challenge. Rather, I legitimately wanted another child. We had more love to spread and share with another baby, and we wanted to welcome another sibling into our kids' lives as they thrived with the arrival of Phoebe. My kids loved being older siblings and always wanted more babies around the house. I envisioned a large family, with a ton of boisterous children making lots of noise in the house. Deep down inside I craved this chaos and thrived on it. So began our fourth and final journey.

In the winter of 2017, I started to feel exhausted and felt like my boobs were a bit sore. Given that we hadn't officially started "trying," I was amazed when I took a test and learned I was pregnant. I couldn't have been more surprised or happier, until I lost the baby two weeks later. Shortly after this miscarriage, I started to really pay attention to my body and what was happening each month. I began tracking my ovulation and period timelines and came to recognize patterns in my cycle. After doing a lot of research and reading everything that I could find on the internet, I ended up diagnosing myself with a short luteal phase defect. I mean, at this point, I was basically a doctor, right?

I called Dr. B, my ob-gyn, and ran my self-diagnosed analysis by her. I explained everything that had happened in the past few months in detail, and she agreed with my thought process. I asked if she could prescribe progesterone for me to use twenty-four hours after ovulation in hopes that it would help me sustain a pregnancy. She agreed this could help and at the very least most definitely wouldn't hurt.

And then, BAM! Progesterone for the win. That did the trick. Immediately I became pregnant with our second boy, Turner Elson O'Neil, who joined our family on January 3, 2019. Turner is our baby who we all dote on and adore. He is the caboose that we dreamed of and his siblings couldn't have relished his arrival more. His many baby milestones over the first couple years of his life are what got us through COVID. He brought such happiness and love into our home during a time where the outside world seemed uncertain. His siblings' love for him is endless and they watch out for him like he is the Pope. We had officially become the family we dreamed of. Two boys and two girls, and two parents who are still in awe of their good fortune and these miraculous kids. Our family was complete.

---

Not a day goes by where we don't marvel at our luck and our beautiful children. Family is everything to us, a sentiment that has only been strengthened by enduring infertility and all its challenges. Let me say it again, family is everything. Everything worth fighting for and everything worth enduring pain for. At the end of the day, family is all we have. And I feel so incredibly blessed to have mine.

We count our blessings every day, but that does not mean that some days are not extremely tough. I mean, hello, COVID. But, even during COVID when we were all cooped up for those long home-schooled weeks, it never left me that I was and am so lucky.

My crazy mind wishes I were younger and could be a gestational carrier for someone struggling. But unfortunately, I am old in terms of fertility so being a surrogate is not possible for me and never was once I finished having children. Lauren and I have always struggled with how to pay it forward, how to help others. The only way we know how is to share our struggles and our story.

We want to try to give people hope when all else fails because that hope comes and goes throughout the long, arduous process of infertility. But if our book can provide a period of hope for someone, then that's something. It's something that we needed many times during our journeys.

# 20

# LAUREN: THE NATURALS

When Caroline was eighteen months old, I told Mackey that I wanted to have another baby. And I wanted to carry that baby on my own.

Brady was doing great—starting to hit his developmental milestones and enrolled in a preschool that was geared toward children with hearing loss. He still had extensive speech and physical therapies, but he was making huge strides. He would likely be able to go to our neighborhood preschool the following year.

I had been doing a lot of research about cervical cerclages—stitching the cervix to prevent a premature birth. Studies had shown that when performed at twelve to fourteen weeks gestation, cervical cerclages had high success rates, especially with singletons.

My previous cerclage, which had been an emergency, was done at twenty weeks because we did not know that I had an incompetent cervix. Although Dr. K had painted a discouraging picture two years prior, predicting that I could get to at least twenty-eight weeks, I had faith in the recent research I was discovering, and faith in my body.

I scheduled an appointment with Dr. Y at Shady Grove Fertility to discuss my options. He had previously worked with Becky and me, and I had grown to love his caring nature.

I arrived at my appointment and was told that I would first have a sonogram to take a look at my uterus.

"Sure, no problem," I said, all the while thinking, *You are not going to find much going on in there.* We started the sono and after a minute or two, the technician casually asked, "When was your last period?"

I told her that I had gotten my period six weeks before, and that happened to be the first time I had menstruated in about fifteen years.

Just then, Dr. Y entered the room. "Okey dokey, my friend, let's have a look here," he said in a sing-song voice, putting a smile on my face. I noticed that they both began whispering about something on the screen.

"Whatcha seeing in there guys?" I asked. "Pretty sure it's like the Sahara Desert down there."

Dr. Y explained that there was a small ball of tissue in my uterus, likely just something left over from my pregnancy with Brady and Jud. He casually added, "We are going to get some bloodwork done and we should know more then."

Hmmm, this sounded very suspicious to me. Not bad suspicious though. They didn't seem alarmed about anything, quite the opposite actually. Soon after, I got dressed, left the office and went back to work.

At about 1:00 p.m. that day I got a phone call from Dr. Y. "Lauren, how are you feeling?" he asked.

"Fine," I told him. "Why?"

"Just wondering if you are feeling tired or anything like that?"

"No, I mean maybe a little, I'm pretty much exhausted 24/7 these days. Why do you ask?"

"Because you are pregnant."

My mouth nearly dropped to the floor. I couldn't speak. What? What did he just say? I had gotten one quick period, had ovulated only once, and now I was pregnant? I couldn't get pregnant for the life of me. This kind of phenomenon didn't happen to me, these were the stories I heard about other people. *Stunned* is the only word I can use that describes how I felt.

Dr. Y explained to me that when they saw the ball of tissue on the sonogram, they suspected I was pregnant, but they didn't want to get my hopes up. He wanted to wait on the bloodwork to confirm. This man knew my history and wasn't about to throw out the word *pregnant* unless he was absolutely positive.

While I had short bouts of nausea in my first trimester, I was pretty much on cloud nine for the entire pregnancy. I had actually gotten pregnant naturally. I truly could not believe that my body was doing this on its own. At thirteen weeks I had my cervical cerclage and was told to take it easy and not work out or lift anything heavy. Fine by me! Gym membership canceled, check.

I continued to go to the high-risk OB unit where they monitored my cervix every other week. Best case scenario I would get to thirty-seven weeks' gestation, at which point they would perform a C-section. They were going to take the baby out a few weeks early to ensure that my membranes didn't rupture or the cerclage didn't break. The baby would also be fully "cooked" at this point, an important consideration.

Compared to the last time, this pregnancy was a dream. Although I was worried that the baby would be born prematurely, my biweekly check-ups continued to confirm that the cerclage was holding and that I was in good shape. I was also not on the dreaded bedrest.

Cole Austin Cronin was born on October 19, 2015, at thirty-seven weeks and five days gestation. It was a straightforward C-section and for some reason I was as calm as a cucumber. We had not known the sex of the baby ahead of time, and when they put that tiny baby boy on my chest in the delivery room, my heart exploded. I had carried him to full term, and he was healthy. He was my impossible that became possible. I spent the entire three months of maternity leave lying in bed staring at him and snuggling. He soon became our "Colie Bear" and the third musketeer of the Cronin trio.

Mackey, Brady, Lauren, Cole, Caroline, now a family of five, the day after Cole's birth.

Life with three kids, while also working full-time, was nuts. These little monsters were not the docile children you sometimes see at the grocery store, quietly walking by their mother's side. No, they were wild, getting into anything they could get their hands on. They were mini terrorists who demanded every minute of our time and energy. And they were loud. So very, very loud. They looked and behaved more like triplets rather than siblings spaced two years apart. There was constant fighting and screaming, wrestling, trips to the ER for stitches, and lots of tears. It was three years of slightly controlled chaos.

---

Despite all of this, I wanted another child. I loved the chaos of a large family. The love I felt for these little people was beyond comprehension; being a mother exceeded all of my expectations and filled me with a sense of purpose.

"Laur, I think we have a good thing going here, but if we want to try, and it happens naturally, I'm in," Mackey said to me one summer night, as we were sitting on our back porch.

Cole was approaching three years old and was starting to be more self-sufficient. If there was a time, it was now. Unfortunately, I hadn't gotten my period in three and a half years, so I wasn't sure how a pregnancy was just going to happen when I wasn't ovulating. My years of infertility at least taught me that.

In November of 2018, Mackey and I booked a sailing trip down to the British Virgin Islands for five days. We invited my parents, Sue and Bob, at the last minute, deciding that we needed a few more hands on deck. They were also a guaranteed good time; they could go head-to-head with us in the "crushing rum punches" category. And the trip was perfect.

Talk about the most relaxing time ever. There was nothing to do but stare out at the gorgeous blue waters, backdropping to craggy mountains against the expansive cloud-dotted sky, deciding what island to visit each day. There was no stress, not a care in the world. (Nurse Judy, Brady's NICU nurse, was watching the three kids at home.)

Mom took on the role of cook/bartender, and I quickly felt like a kid again as she grilled burgers in the galley and mixed my cocktails. I quickly morphed into my six-year-old self where my mom was doing everything for me. She was lucky I didn't start calling her Mommy again. It was pure bliss.

Fast-forward five weeks later. I was running errands on a Wednesday morning, and in the span of twenty minutes I had two quick bouts of nausea (I also stopped for two bacon-egg-and-cheese bagel sandwiches and a large Coke as a midmorning snack). After the second wave of nausea, a light went off in my head. Could it be? Not a chance, I told myself.

But then I found myself swerving into the closest CVS parking lot, running inside to buy a pregnancy test, and peeing on the stick in their public bathroom. A girl has got to know.

And there it was, plain as day, positively pregnant. I sat in that bathroom for ten more minutes, literally not believing what I was seeing. I ran out of the stall, bought another test, and took that one. Clear as day, pregnant.

Thinking back on this moment now, I can't stress to you how lucky I feel. After going through all of those years of stress and suffering and there I was getting pregnant naturally for the second time. I simply could not believe how things had turned for Mackey and me. The gratitude that I felt at that moment was all encompassing.

I ran right to Lacey's house. She was pregnant with Turner at the time, and we basically just sat on her bed and smiled at each other.

Mackey was out of town for work and was returning home late the following night. It was not in my nature to be able to keep this news from him, but I wanted to see the look on his face when I told him. I waited up for him to come home and when he did, I handed him a small "early Christmas present." He looked at me oddly and began to open the positive pregnancy stick that I had saved.

"What the—" were the first words out of his mouth, followed by a tear of joy, and then a look of sheer fear that read "Um, I'm going to be a father of four?" He was thrilled, and we sat and marveled at how we had gotten to this point after so many years.

The pregnancy was uneventful except for the fact that I felt like complete dogshit for the first fifteen weeks. I looked like a character out of *Night of the Living Dead*. I got my cervical cerclage at thirteen weeks and by week sixteen, I was feeling good again. When I was pregnant with Cole, I was in a constant state of worry over whether I would deliver early. I basically tiptoed around for thirty-seven weeks. But with this pregnancy, history was on my side, and I was confident that I would make it full term.

Once again, we decided that the sex of the baby would be a surprise. When they pulled her out and yelled, "It's a girl!" I was over the moon. I was especially grateful that I now had "my girls," just as my mother had Lacey and me. And Caroline would get the truly magical gift of a sister named Neile.

# POSTSCRIPT

So here we are, the two Aumiller sisters, no longer bitches on IVF, but fully engaged moms. More than fifteen years have passed since we started our frequently treacherous infertility journeys, and now we have eight children between us. Lacey's eldest, Milly, is now eleven years old, followed by Bo (ten), Phoebe (eight), and Turner (four). Brady (eleven) is Lauren's firstborn. Tragically, his twin brother, Jud, died in infancy. But he now has three siblings: Caroline (nine), Cole (seven), and Neile (four).

We both dreamed of having large families and are thrilled that our dreams have come true. But it took a lot of work and perseverance, which thankfully paid off, despite many, many setbacks and hardships. It's not that we don't get bitchy or angry at times. Raising children, especially during COVID, can be pure hell.

The phone rings and without even looking, Lauren knows it is Lacey. "Shoot me," she says, as she answers the phone.

"Yup, this struggle is real, sista," says Lace, and immediately they start laughing about the pure chaos of their mornings. Schools are closed due to the pandemic and each sister is homeschooling the children and hating every second of it. They agree to head to the bike trail at lunchtime, once the kids are done with online classes. It means hauling a bunch of bikes, strollers, and food for ten up to the park. But at least our outing will get everyone out of the house and we can talk to each other while the kids let off their energy.

———

We meet up in the parking lot and start unloading all the bikes. The kids bound out of the car and immediately flail themselves upon one another. Their need for human interaction, especially with their cousins, is crucial during this time of isolation. They can't get enough.

We look at each other and smile. We both know exactly what the other is thinking. We have come so far. We have both been through some hellish times, but we dug deep, and look where we are today. We have eight bright, amazing, wild kids between us. They challenge us each and every day, at some points driving us to complete insanity, but my God, are they special.

We fought for each one of them, and we never need to be reminded how fortunate we are to have them. We are so lucky to have these families that seemed so far off in the past. And we are so lucky to have each other, to be able to raise our families alongside one another. As if our bond wasn't strong enough from our four decades as sisters, these eight kids and the many journeys we endured—with Becky as our mutual angel/surrogate for Milly and Caroline—have brought us even closer.

Not a day goes by that we both don't share our stories with someone, or that we don't lend an ear to a friend or stranger who is having a difficult time conceiving. We have found that the need to vent to others who have navigated the infertility struggle and who have come out on the other end of it is deep and crucial. This is the reason that we wanted to share our story—to give hope to those who are having problems getting pregnant and feel alone in their struggle.

Our most fervent wish is that you know you are not alone. There are so many women who feel exactly like you do. If only there were more "Bitches on IVF" bumper stickers on cars, ev-

From left, Lauren, Becky, Lacey (back row), Caroline and Milly (front row).

eryone would realize how many strong-ass women are engaged in this struggle. Having others to relate to and lean on can help make the journey less painful and, hopefully, more fruitful.

Although it is hard, and at times lonely and depressing, we truly believe that if you want a family, and you are willing to fight for it, you will achieve your goal. Whether it be IVF, surrogacy, or adoption, there is a path for you, should you choose to pursue it. Keep your head up, your heart open, and your arms ready to hold that baby.

We hope that by sharing our story, at least one person will take a deep breath and know that they are not alone. Know there are always brighter days ahead and give hope to those who are struggling. Remember, there are always rainbows after rain. Dig deep and find your rainbow. One of our favorite sayings sums it up quite nicely: "Difficult things take a long time; impossible things take a little longer."

Cronin family, on a cross-country trip, July 2021.

O'Neil family, summer 2023.

# ACKNOWLEDGMENTS

We would like to thank all of those people who helped make this book possible. First and foremost, our friend, Erin Rothwell. If it wasn't for your push and those early days of organizing our book, we would never have completed this project. You always loved and believed in the power of our story, and we are so grateful for your support. Your creativity, energy, and ability to bring this book to life is what propelled us forward. We will never forget your contribution and enthusiasm. You are a true gem.

We would also like to thank our editors. Joan Smith Liebmann, you were a joy to work with. Being so far but always feeling so close. We looked forward to your ideas and suggestions and always valued your opinion. We continue to wait for the day when we are drinking wine together in NYC.

To editor Sandra Wendel, our fairy godmother. This book would never have been published without you, truly. Your humor and straightforwardness were always welcome attributes. Even if you did delete over 300 exclamation marks. This one's for you!

To the countless nurses, doctors, therapists, and healthcare workers who stood by on this journey. We will never forget the compassion and empathy you so generously showered over us. We are forever grateful for your support. You are true heroes.

To our parents, Sue and Bob, for their never-ending support

and love. As we've come to learn ourselves, your child is a child for life. No matter their age. We've always felt your unconditional love and support and you've been amazing examples of what a parent should be. And to the rest of our family—siblings and in-laws—thank you for always being there to listen and rally us when we most needed it.

And a huge thank-you to our husbands. Without strong men by our side, none of this would have turned out the way it did. Ben and Mackey, you are our true partners in life, always cheering us on in the good times and the bad. You believed in us when we may not have believed in ourselves. We love you both so much.

Finally, to our eight children. Without you all, we wouldn't be whole. Thank you for making our dreams come true and for fighting your way to be in our lives. We love you with all our hearts. Always and forever.

# ABOUT THE AUTHORS

Lacey and Lauren, also known as the Aumiller sisters for most of their lives, were born and raised outside of Baltimore, Maryland. Their bond as sisters has been one of the most deeply gratifying experiences in each of their lives.

**Lacey Aumiller O'Neil** is what some would call a supermom who wears many hats. At forty-four years young, she is the proud mother of four amazing children who keep her on her toes. Lacey's greatest joy is staying home to raise her little ones, a job that is both challenging and rewarding.

Her journey to motherhood wasn't easy, but now she's making the most of it. Lacey is actively involved in her children's school and dedicates countless hours to coaching her daughters' club lacrosse teams. She is often found running and loves a good half marathon race. Lacey and her husband, Ben, share a passion for sports, which they love to pass on and do with their kids.

Prior to raising her family, Lacey worked in real estate and lived in Washington, DC, and Annapolis, Maryland before settling in Baltimore. She is a graduate of the University of Virginia, where she played lacrosse and met Ben O'Neil. They both love spending time and creating memories with their family in both Fenwich Island, Delaware and Pentwater, Michigan.

**Lauren Aumiller Cronin** is a forty-two-year-old mother of four rambunctious kids, who has had a successful career in both finance and real estate. She attended the University of Virginia, where she played lacrosse for four years and was a member of the US Women's Lacrosse Team from 1999 to 2004. Lauren's love of sports has continued throughout her life, but you are more likely to find her on a yoga mat or in the water surfing than on a lacrosse field. Or in the kitchen baking—and then eating those baked goods.

She and her husband, Mackey, love to travel with their kids to show them all that this beautiful world has to offer. On their bucket list is a sailing trip around the world as a family of six, without killing each other. After a two-year "adventure" in San Diego, they recently moved back to Baltimore to reunite the cousins and be closer to what they value most: family.

These sisters have done everything together throughout their lives, including infertility. After telling people their story, time and time again, the sole reaction was "you two have to write a book." It was never their intention to put pen to paper, but the more they thought about it, they came to love the idea.

To be able to help people who are struggling with infertility seemed like a small way to give back. They want to inspire, motivate, and help those suffering find determination to keep up the fight against infertility. They hope you find this book funny, insightful, impactful, terrifying, sad, but, most importantly, inspirational. Because at the end of the day, if there is a will, there is a way.

Made in United States
North Haven, CT
18 May 2024

52654663R00114